感受英语的魅力　智慧英文　励志篇　体验英语的快乐

我爱│英文

美国英语语言协会 (强力推荐)

生命不息，奋斗不止

Where There is Life There is Struggle

★语言学习者阅读本书，可以提高文学素养，开阔视野，陶冶情操
★翻译爱好者阅读本书，可以将经典原文和优美的译文对比推敲，欣赏佳译

英语学习最佳读本
雄视教辅书界「畅销3年」

刘彦军　高华军◎主编

北京燕山出版社

图书在版编目(CIP)数据

生命不息,奋斗不止:英汉对照/刘彦军,高华军主编.—北京:北京燕山出版社,2009.9 (2011 年 7 月重印)

(智慧英文.励志篇)

ISBN 978 - 7 - 5402 - 2116 - 4

Ⅰ.生… Ⅱ.①刘…②高… Ⅲ.①英语 - 汉语 - 对照读物②成功心理学 - 青少年读物 Ⅳ.H319.4:B

中国版本图书馆 CIP 数据核字(2009)第 141289 号

生命不息,奋斗不止

责任编辑:	孙婷/马明仁
出版发行:	北京燕山出版社
社　　址:	北京市宣武区陶然亭路 53 号
邮政编码:	100054
印　　刷:	大厂县回族自治县正兴印务有限公司
经　　销:	全国新华书店
开　　本:	700×1000　1/16
印　　张:	160
印　　次:	2011 年 7 月第 2 次印刷
书　　号:	ISBN 978 - 7 - 5402 - 2115 - 7
定　　价:	258.00 元(全十册)

　　本系列丛书在编著过程中,由于时间仓促,工作量大,未能及时与部分所选文章的作者一一取得联系,本着对书稿质量的追求,又不忍将美文割爱,故冒昧地将文章选录书中。

　　请有关作者在见到本书后,主动与我们联系。

目 录

CONTENT

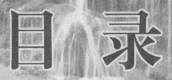

目录

CONTENT

目 录

CONTENT

目录

CONTENT

目录

CONTENT

目录

CONTENT

目 录

CONTENT

目录

CONTENT

乡村的秋日

佚名

小时候,我认为乡村的秋天是最悲哀的季节,因此根本不喜欢秋天。每当秋风吹起,落叶飘飘,我总是敲打着窗台,大喊:"讨厌的风,滚开! "

对于像我这么大的孩子来说,树上的树叶是那么青翠,那么欢乐。它们就像我的玩具消防车、暖和的手套、妈妈的玫瑰,可是无情的秋风带走了这美丽的一切。

我不知道,秋天的树叶完成了为大树提供养分的使命,甚至不懂得明年夏天树上会长出更多的叶片。

当我再长大一点,就不讨厌烧树叶发出的味道了。我知道,明年还会长出更多的树叶,开放更多的花儿,有更多的绿阴让鸟儿做窝。

我记得在很小的时候,一个寒冷的秋天的早晨,我急急忙忙地走出屋外,敲碎了水盆上的冰块。平时小鸟都是在里面嬉水,今天等了半天也看不到小鸟的影子。妈妈说小鸟都飞到温暖的南方去了,明年春天才会回来。爸爸也这么说。我却不能相信。这么小的小鸟,还没有我的手掌大,怎么能像飞机一样飞到遥远的南方去呢?

现在,当我看到一群小鸟排成整齐的V字形向南方飞去的时候,就为它们,也为自己高兴。我知道它们来年还会回来,从南方回来的时候身体都会很健壮。它们会飞回来装点我们门前的树木,会像主人一样在春天的草坪上自由自在地漫步。

秋天的池塘像一面镜子,一切都是那么平静,只有轻快的浮云倒影掠过。

在我很小的时候,总是用一根小棍扰动池水。因为我想念那些青蛙、乌龟和小鱼,想把它们全部唤醒。爸爸说它们在池底睡觉,真庆幸我的打扰没有把它们吵醒。

现在我知道了,所有的生命都需要安静、温暖和黑暗。而这一切只有在秋日的池塘深处才能够找到。它们需要时间来成长,因此我打算等待。向秋天说再见,我们还会再见。

Autumn in the Country

Anonymous

When I was very young, I thought autumn in the country was the saddest time. I didn't like it one bit. When the wind blew the leaves off the trees, I used to bang on the window and say, "Bad wind, go away! "

To a little child, such as I was then, the leaves looked so bright and happy. They were the colour of my toy fire truck and warm mittens and Mom's roses. The wind seemed mean as it ripped away at them.

I didn't know that by autumn the leaves had done all the work they could do. (Leaves help make food for the tree.) I didn't even know that there would be more leaves next summer.

Now that I'm more grown up, I don't mind the smell of the smoke that rises from a pile of fuming autumn leaves. I know that there will be more leaves and blossoms and shady places for birds to build their nests in.

One autumn when I was very young, I remember hurrying outside on a frosty morning to break the crust of ice that covered the birdbath. Then I ran back into the house and peered out the window to watch all the birds playing in the water. Hardly any did. Mom explained that most of the birds had flown south to be warm. Mom said they'd be back next spring. Dad said so, too. I didn't really believe it. How could those birds, some of them smaller than my hand, fly as far as big airplanes fly?

智慧英文励志篇

Now when I see a flock of birds heading south in a V as neat as an arrow,

I'm happy for them and for me, too. I know that they'll return all strong and healthy and decorate our trees and strut across our spring lawn as if they owned the place.

In autumn our pond is as still as a mirror. Nothing seems to move in it except the reflection of the fluid, floating clouds.

When I was very young, I used to stir the pond with a stick. I missed the frogs and turtles and fish, I wanted to wake them up. Dad said they were asleep down at the bottom of the pond, Luckily, my stick wasn't very long, and nothing happened.

Now I know that all those creatures need the quiet and warmth and darkness that can be found only deep in our pond in the autumn. They need a time to grow. So I'm going to wait.

Saying goodbye in autumn isn't saying goodbye forever.

月出

佚名

我常在晚上爬上我家附近的一座小山。在山上，城市的喧嚣退为远远的低语。在静谧的黑夜中，我可以感受蟋蟀的快乐、猫头鹰的自信。但是我爬山是为了观赏月出，可以再次获得在城市中轻易失去的安静和清新。

我已经在这座山上看过很多次月出。每次月亮的外貌和性情都不相同。秋天丰盈的月亮充满着自信；春天雾蒙蒙的月亮羞怯不已；冬天的月亮孤寂地悬挂在黑沉沉的夜空中；昏黄的夏月朦朦胧胧，遥对着干燥的原野。每一个时候，月亮都像美妙的音乐，震撼我的心灵、抚慰我的灵魂。

赏月自古就有。在古代猎人的眼中，天上的月亮就像心跳一样准确。他们知道每隔二十九天月亮就会由明亮圆满变得纤细，直至消失，然后再次重现；他们知道，月盈的时候，每次日落，头上的月亮都会变得更加高远硕大；他们还知道，月亏的时候，月出会一天比一天晚，直到有一天太阳升起的时候仍然看不到月亮的踪影。古人能够凭借经验知道月亮的变化轨迹，真是让人难以置信。

但是我们由于居住在室内而与月亮失去了联系。城市刺眼的街灯和污浊的烟尘遮蔽了夜空。人类虽然曾经登上过月球，但对于我们，月亮却变得更加陌生了。有几个人能够说清今夜的月亮什么时候能够升空？

但是无论怎样，月亮依然影响着我们的心灵。如果偶尔看到刚升起的巨大而金黄的满月，谁都会停下脚步凝神观望她的无上尊容。而月亮也会祝福那些注视她的人们。

我体会到月亮的馈赠是在一个七月的山间夜晚。我的车突然熄火了，我孤身一人被困在山中。太阳已经落山，我看到东边山上涌现一团明亮的橘黄色光芒，好像森林起火一般。转眼山上仿佛也迸射出火焰。一会儿，月亮从森林中露出了大而红的脸，夏天空气中弥漫的雾气和潮气使得月亮仿佛有点扭曲变形。

大地滚烫的呼吸扭曲了月亮。她变得不再美丽，性情暴躁。附近农家的狗都紧张地叫了起来，认为这样奇怪的亮光惊醒了野草中的魔鬼。

　　然而，当月亮慢慢离开山头，她开始显得坚定而庄严，面孔也由红色变成橘黄，然后变成金色，最后变成平静的黄色。随着月亮的升高，下面的丘陵山谷逐渐变得模糊不清，好像大地的亮光都被月亮吸去。等到皓月当空，圆满的月亮撒下象牙一般洁白的光辉，月光下的山谷便成为了一片片幽深的阴影。那些狗发现光亮来自它们所熟悉的月亮，也就停止了吠叫，安定下来。这时候我也觉得突然增添了很多信心，心情愉悦，甚至情不自禁地笑了出来。

　　这样幻美的景色持续了一个小时。充满魔力的月亮缓缓出现。这样的观赏我们必须要回到过去那种对时间的耐心中去。看着月亮无拘无束地上升让我们内心得到少有的安宁，我们的思想能够让我们发现宇宙的宏伟和大地的辽阔，能让我们忘却自身。我们觉得渺小，但又深感大自然的厚爱。

　　月光抹去了生活中坚硬的棱角，为山谷披上了银色的轻纱，海水变成静谧的深蓝，沉浸在月光中的我们不再像平时一样斤斤计较，而是陶醉在自然的氛围中。

　　正当我沉醉在这美丽的月色中时，神奇的事情发生了。那个七月的夜晚，在看了两个钟头的月亮之后，我回到汽车里，再次发动汽车。发动机居然开始发动，像几个小时之前的熄火一样神秘而突然。我沿着山路开车回家，肩上披着明月，心中一片安详。

　　后来我经常来到山上看月出。当烦心事接踵而来时，尤其是在秋天，常常会让人疲惫不堪，这时我就爬上那座小山，等待那轮金色之月照耀大地，为黑夜洒下光明。

　　一只猫头鹰从山上飞下，静静地，却在月光中火一样掠过。一只蟋蟀在草丛中大声放歌。这使我想起了诗人以及音乐家，想起了贝多芬的《月光奏鸣曲》和莎士比亚笔下《威尼斯商人》中洛伦佐的话："沉睡岸边的月光如此甜蜜/我们要坐在这里/让音乐之声潜入我们的耳朵。"我不知道他们的诗作和音乐，也像那蟋蟀的歌声一样，可以算作月亮的声音。想到这里，城市生活给我带来的混乱心情便沉浸在了这安宁的夜色中。

　　相爱的人和诗人在夜里能够体会到更深刻的生活意义。其实我们都爱问一些深刻的问题——我们的祖先是谁?我们的命运将会怎样?我们愿意沉沦在这些没有答案的问题中，而不喜欢那些统治着白天世界的没有情感的几何教科书。到了晚上，我们都变成了哲人和神秘主义者。

　　月亮升起的时候，我们放缓了思想，让它跟随天堂的脚步。突然间，魔力流遍周身。我们打开情感的阀门，让平日被理智所禁锢的那部分思绪尽情奔涌。通过遥远的距离，我们听到古代猎人的低语，看到远古的诗人和爱侣们眼中的世界。

Spell of the Rising Moon

Anonymous

There is a hill near my home that I often climb at night. The noise of the city is a far—off murmur. In the hush of dark I share the cheerfulness of crickets and the confidence of owls. But it is the drama of the moonrise that I come to see. For that restores in me a quiet and clarity that the city spends too freely.

From this hill I have watched many moons rise. Each one had its own mood. There have been broad, confident harvest moons in autumn; shy, misty moons in spring; lonely, winter moons rising into the utter silence of an ink black sky and smoke—smudged orange moons over the dry fields of summer.Each, like fine music, excited my heart and then calmed my soul.

Moon gazing is an ancient art. To prehistoric hunters the moon overhead was as unerring as heartbeat. They knew that every 29 days it become full—bellied and brilliant, then sickened and died, and then was reborn. They knew the waxing moon appeared larger and higher overhead after each succeeding sunset. They knew the waning moon rose later each night until it vanished in the sunrise. To have understood the moon's patterns from experience must been a profound thing.

But we, who live indoors, have lost contact with the moon, The glare of street lights and the dust of pollution veil the night sky. Though men have walked on the moon, it grows less

智慧英文励志篇

familiar. Few of us can say when the moon will rise tonight.

Still, it tugs at our minds, If we unexpectedly encounter the full moon,huge and yellow over the horizon, we are helpless but to stare back at its commanding presence. And the moon has gifts to bestow upon those who watch.

I learned about its gifts one July evening in the mountains. My car had mysteriously stalled, and I was stranded and alone. The sun had set, and I was watching what seemed to be the bright—orange glow of a forest fire beyond a ridge to the east. Suddenly, the ridge itself seemed to burst into flame: Then,the rising moon, huge and red and grotesquely misshapen by the dust and sweat of the summer atmosphere, loomed up out of the woods.

Distorted thus by the hot breath of earth, the moon seemed ill—tempered and imperfect. Dogs at nearby farmhouses barked nervously, as if this strange light had wakened evil spirits in the weeds.

But as the moon lifted off the ridge it gathered firmness and authority. Its complexion changed from red, to orange, to gold, to impassive yellow. It seemed to draw light out of the darkening earth, for as it rose, the hills and valleys below grew dimmer. By the time the moon stood clear of the horizon,full chested and round and the color of ivory, the valleys were deep shadows in the landscape. The dogs, reassured that this was the familiar moon, stopped barking. And all at once I felt a confidence and joy close to laughter.

The drama took an hour. Moonrise is slow and serried with subtleties. To watch it, we must slip into an older, more patient sense of time. To watch the moon move inexorably higher is to find an unusual stillness within ourselves.Our imaginations become aware of the vast distances of space, the immensity of the earth and huge improbability of our own existence. We feel small but privileged.

Moonlight shows us none of life's harder edges. Hillsides seem silken and silvery, the oceans still and blue in its light. In moonlight we become less calculating, more drawn to our feelings.

And odd things happen in Such moments. On that July night, I watched the moon for an hour or two, and then got back into the car, turned the key in the igttition and heard the engine start, just as mysteriously as it had stalled a few hours earlier I drove down from the mountains with the moon on my shoulder and peace in my heart.

I return often to the rising moon. I am draw especially when events crowd ease and clarity of vision into a small comer of my life. This happens often in the fall. Then I go to my hill and await the hunter's moon, enormous and gold over the horizon, filling, the night with vision.

An owl swoops from the ridgetop, noiseless but bright as flame. A cricket shrills in the grass. I think of poets and musicians. Of Beethoven's "Moonlight Sonata" and of Shakespeare, whose Lorenzo declaims in The Merchant of Venice, "How sweet the moonlight sleeps upon this bank! /Here will we sit and let the sounds of music/Creep in our ears." I wonder if their verse and music,like the music of crickets, are in some way voices of the moon. With such thoughts, my citified confusions melt into the quiet of the night.

Lovers and poets find deeper meaning at night. We are all apt to pose deeper questions—about our origins and destinies. We indulge in riddles, rather than in the impersonal geometries that govern the day–lit world. We become philosophers and mystics.

At moonrise, as we slow our minds to the pace of the heavens, enchantment steals over us. We open the vents of feeling and exercise parts of our minds that reason locks away by day. We hear, across the distances, murmurs of ancient hunter and see anew the visions of poets and lovers of long ago.

心灵深处

佚名

　　这个故事讲述了一个军人在越南战争后，终于可以回家的事。他从旧金山给父母打电话说："爸，妈，我就要回来了，但我想求你们一件事，我想带一个朋友回家。""可以啊，"他们异口同声地答道，"我们很高兴能见到他。"

　　"有件事情，我应该告诉你们，"儿子继续说，"他在战斗中受了重伤，失去了一个胳膊和一条腿，他无处可去，我想带他回去和我们一起生活。"

　　"儿子，听到这些我们感觉很难过。或许，我们可以帮他找到别的安身立命之所。""不，爸妈，我就是想让他和我们生活在一起。""儿子啊，"爸爸语重心长地说："你难道不明白这个要求对我们意味着什么吗?这样的残障人会给我们的生活带来许多难以想象的负担，我们自己还要生活，不能让这样的事情打破我们正常的生活，我认为你倒是应该马上回来，把你的同伴忘记吧，他会想办法走好自己的路。"

　　听完这些话，儿子挂断了电话，此后便杳无音信。几天后，他的父母接到了一个来自旧金山警署的电话。警察说，他们的儿子从一幢高楼上跌下来，死了。警察确认这是一起自杀事件。悲痛欲绝的父母当即飞往旧金山，去停尸房认领尸体。他们认出了儿子，然而，出乎意料的是，他只有一个胳膊和一条腿。

Look in Your Heart

Anonymous

A story is told about a soldier who was finally coming home after having fought in Vietnam. He called his parents from San Francisco. "Mom and Dad, I'm coming home, but I've a favor to ask. I have a friend I'd like to bring home with me." "Sure," they replied, "we'd love to meet him."

"There's something you should know" , the son continued, "he was hurt pretty badly in the fighting. He stepped on a land mind and lost an arm and a leg. He has nowhere else to go, and I want him to come live with us."

"I'm sorry to hear that, son. Maybe we can help him find somewhere to live." "No, Mom and Dad, I want him to live with us." "Son," said the father, "you don't know what you're asking. Someone with such a handicap would be a terrible burden on us. We have our own lives to live, and we can't let something like this interfere with our lives. I think you should just come home and forget about this guy. He'll find a way to live on his own."

At that point, the son hung up the phone. The parents heard nothing more from him. A few days later, however, they received a call from the San Francisco police.Their son had died after falling from a building, they were told. The police believed it was suicide. The grief—stricken parents flew to San Francisco and were taken to the city morgue to identify the body of their son. They recognized him, but to their horror they also discovered something they didn't know, their son had only one arm and one leg.

长途货车司机的临终遗言

鲁德·肯德尔

斯廷博特山是人类的克星，行驶在阿拉斯加公路上的长途货车司机们无不望而生畏，特别是在冬季,司机们更是对它畏惧三分。这里的山路崎岖蜿蜒,覆盖冰层的公路旁边就是陡峭的悬崖。无数货车连人带车翻下山去,类似的事故不断重演。

一次,我在阿拉斯加公路行驶时,遇到了加拿大皇家骑警队,几辆救援车正吊起一辆挂在峭壁半中央的货车残骸。旁边站着很多路过的司机,他们默默地看着失事的货车被缓缓吊起。我停下车,向人群走去。

一名骑警向我们走来,低声说:"很遗憾,我们发现这位货车司机时,他已经死了。两天前,这里有一场暴风雪,他肯定是在那时翻下悬崖的。"

"这里有封信,你们可以看看。我想,他在冻死前还活了几个小时。"

我从未见过警察哭——我一直认为,他们对死亡和绝望已司空见惯,早就麻木了,但他把信递给我时,我分明看见他在擦眼泪。读着读着,我也不禁潸然泪下。司机们轮流默默地读完信,然后静静回到各自的车上。那封信的内容深深地刻在了我的记忆里,即使几年后的今天也依然清晰在目,好像我正拿着它读一样。所以,我很想你们及你们的家人也都来读读这封信。

我的爱妻:

谁也不愿意写这样的信,但我还算幸运,还有足够的时间把那些我多次忘记对你说的话告诉你。亲爱的,我爱你。

你常开玩笑说,我爱这车比爱你多,因为很多时候我都是和它在一起。是的,我确实很喜欢这铁家伙——它对我一直很好,我们共同走过了很多地方,度过了很多艰难的日子。不论是长途跋涉还是在坦途上急速行驶,它从来没让我失望过。

可你知道吗?多少艰难的岁月,我们也是这样挺过来的。也正是这个原因,我爱你。

此刻,我想起了你为我所舍弃的一切——服装、假期、聚会、朋友。对此,你毫无怨言,而我却从未向你道过谢。

我和儿子们坐下喝咖啡时,我总谈论我的车及为其所花的钱。我想,我是忘记你是我妻子了。虽然你没和我一起坐在车上,但为了攒钱买新车,你的牺牲和决心绝不亚于我。

买了新车,我无比自豪。当然,我也为你而自豪,只是我从未说过,我以为你知道。如果以前我能用与擦车同样多的时间和你聊聊天,或许我会说。

开货车的这些年,我知道你一直都在为我祈祷。可这次,你的祈祷还是未能使我幸免于难。

我伤得很严重,已经走到生命的尽头。过去,我太在意车和工作,因而,那些早该说很多次的话和抛之脑后的事,我现在想说说。

很多次,我都忘记了结婚纪念日和家人的生日。多少次,因为我出车在外,儿子的学校演出和曲棍球赛,你就只能一个人去。

多少个孤单的夜晚,你挂念着我。很多次我想给你打电话问好,却又没打。想到你和孩子们在家等候着我的归来,我内心平静、了无牵挂。

当我把车开进院子,看见你正睡在小车上等我,我真为你骄傲。在我眼中,不论是凌晨两点还是下午两点,你都像个电影明星。你知道吗,你美极了。我想我很久都没跟你这么说过了,但你确实很美。

这一生,我犯的错数不胜数,要说我做过的一个明智选择,算是向你求婚了。你可能永远不会明白我为何如此热衷于开货车。坦白说,我也不明白,但这是我生活的方式,于是,你也就顺着我。我们同甘苦、共患难,一路走了过来。亲爱的,我爱你,也爱我们的孩子。

我浑身疼痛不已,但更痛的是心。我们在一起这么久了,但在我生命的最后时刻,你却不在我身旁,我第一次感到孤单,这种感觉太可怕了。我很需要你,但我知道已经太晚了。

也真是有意思,现在我居然是和这车在一起。这么多年来,我都和这个变了形的铁家伙形影不离,这该死的货车占据了我生命中太多的时间。但它不能回报我的爱,只有你能。

虽然你远在千里之外,但我感觉你就在我身旁。我能看到你的面庞,也能感受到你浓浓的爱,可是,想到自己要一个人走完这最后一段路,我还是很害怕。

告诉孩子们,我很爱他们,但别让他们以开车为业。

亲爱的,就说这些吧。上帝啊,我那么爱你,一定要好好照顾自己,别忘了——这辈子,我最爱的是你,只是忘了对你说。

我爱你!

比尔

1974年12月

A Trucker's Last Letter

Rud Kendall

Steamboat Mountain is a man–killer, and truckers who haul the Alaska Highway treat it with respect, particularly in the winter.The road curves and twists over the mountain and sheer cliffs drop away sharply from the icy road. Countless trucks and truckers have been lost there and many more will follow their last tracks.

On one trip up the highway, I came upon the Royal Canadian Mounted Police and several wreckers winchings the remains of a semi–up the steep cliff. I parked my rig and went over to the quiet group of truckers who were watching the wreckage slowly come into sight.

One of the Mounties walked over to us and spoke quietly. "I'm sorry,"he said. "the driver was dead when we found him. He must have gone over the side two days ago when we had a bad snowstorm."

"Here. maybe you guys should read this. I guess he lived for a couple of hours until the cold got to him."

I'd never seen tears in a cop's eyes before— I always figured they'd seen so much death and despair they were immune to it, but he wiped tears as he handed me the letter. As I read it, I began to weep. Each driver silently read the words, then quietly walked back to his rig. The words were burned into my memory and now, years later, that letter is still vivid as if I were holding it before me. I want to share that letter with you and your families.

December, 1974

My Darling Wife,

This is a letter that no man ever wants to write, but I'm lucky enough to have some

智慧英文励志篇

time to say what I've forgotten to say so many times. I love you,sweetheart.

You used to kid that that I loved the truck more than you because I spent more time with her. I do love this piece of iron she's been good to me. She's seen me through a tough times and tough places. I could always count on her in a long haul and she was speedy in the stretches. She never let me down.

But you want to know something? I love you for the same reasons.You've seen me through the tough tithes and places, too.

I think now of all the things you gave up for me. The clothes, the holidays, the parties, the friends. You never complained and somehow I never remembered to thank you for being you.

When I sat having coffee with the boys, I always talked about my truck, my payments. I guess l forgot you were my partner even if you weren't in the cab with me. It was your sacrifices and determination as much as mine that finally got the new truck.

I was so proud of that truck I was bursting. I was proud of you too, but I never told you that. I took it for granted you knew, but ifl had spent as much time talking with you as I did polishing chrome, perhaps I would have.

In all the years I've pounded the pavement, I always knew your prayers rode with me. But this time they weren't enough.

I'm hurt and it's bad. I've made my last mile and I want to say the things that should have been said so many times before. The things that were forgotten because I was too concerned about the truck and the job.

I'm thinking about the missed anniversaries and birthdays. The school plays and hockey games that you went to alone because I was on the road.

I'm thinking about the lonely nights you spent alone, wondering where I was and how things were going. I'm thinking of all the times I thought of calling you just to say hello and somehow didn't get around to.I'm thinking of the peace of mind I had knowing that you were at home with the kids, waiting for me.

I was proud of you when Ipulled into the yard and saw you sleeping in the car waiting for me. Whether it was two in the morning or two in the afternoon you always looked like a

15

movie star to me. You're beautiful you know. I guess I haven't told you that lately, but you are.

I made lots of mistakes in my life, but if I only ever made one good decision, it was when I asked you to marry me. You never could understand what it was that kept me trucking. I couldn't either, but it was my way of life and you stuck with me. Good times, bad times, you were always there. I love you, sweetheart, and I love the kids.

My body hurts but my heart hurts even more. You won't be here when I end this trip. For thefirst time since we've been together, I'm really alone and it scares me. I need you so badly, and I know it's too late.

It's funny I guess, but what I have now is the truck. This damned truck that ruled our lives for so long. This twisted hunk of steel that I lived in and with for so many years. But it can't return my love. Only you can do that.

You're a thousand miles away but I feel you here with me. I can see your face and feel your love and I'm scared to make the final run alone.

Tell the kids that I love them very much and don't let the boys drive any truck for a living.

I guess that's about it, honey. My God, but I love you very much. Take care of yourself and always remember that I loved you more than anything in life. I just forgot to tell you.

I love you,

Bill

温柔

达芙娜·勒南

我和迈克尔坐在纽约市繁华的第三大道的一家小熟食店里，我们几乎没注意到服务员已经把盘子放到了我们的桌上。

也许我们的交流算不上深刻，但至少很生动。我们笑谈前晚看过的电影，讨论文学讨论课上学过的文章的引申含义。他说，他从少年步入成年，拒绝别人叫他"米基"，成为真正的迈克尔时，是12岁还是14岁，他记不清了，但他的确记得母亲曾嚷着嫌他长得太快。我们开始吃蓝莓薄饼卷时，我把我和妹妹去乡下看表姐妹时摘蓝莓的故事讲给他听。记得我总是在回家前把我摘的那些都吃光，而姑姑总告诫我说，那样会肚子疼。当然，我肚子从来就没疼过。

我们的畅谈仍在继续，我环顾了一下餐馆，一对老年夫妇吸引了我的目光，他们坐在一个靠墙角的小餐桌旁。她的那条花裙子和椅垫一样褪了色，旧手提包放在椅垫上。老头有着光泽的头顶，就和他正细嚼慢咽的糖心蛋一样发亮。

她不紧不慢地喝着麦片粥，让人感到单调乏味。

他们不受外界干扰的静默吸引了我的注意。在我眼里，他们那个小小的角落被一种令人忧郁的空虚浸透了。

我和迈克尔继续交谈着，时而欢笑，时而低语，时而表白，时而品评，我却被这对老夫妇透彻的静寂深深触动了。太可悲了，我想，难道真的无话可说了，难道彼此的故事里再没有未敞开的新篇章了吗？倘若我们遇到这样的情景又会怎样呢？

我和迈克尔埋单后起身离开餐馆。我们从老夫妇就坐的角落经过时，我的钱包刚好掉到地上。我弯下身去捡时，发现他们的手温柔地在餐桌下握在一起。他们的手始终这

17

样握着！

　　我站起身，亲眼目睹的朴素而真挚的相依之情，不禁让我感到自惭形秽。老人温柔地爱抚妻子疲惫的手指所流露出的柔情，不仅弥漫在我曾以为是情感空白的角落，也充溢着我的内心。他们的静默并非那种初次约会一句妙语或一段趣闻后令人不舒服的沉默。他们的沉默反而令人很惬意，是一种无需语言表达的温柔之爱。

　　或许他们已经这样共同分享早上的时光好长时间了，今天与昨天相比，并没有什么差别，可他们以平和的心态对待一切，彼此以诚相待。

　　我与迈克尔走出餐馆时，我不禁想，或许有一天，我们也会这样，那未必是件坏事，反倒会是件好事。

A Gentle Caress

Daphna Renan

Michael and I hardly noticed when the waitress came and placed the plates on our table. We were seated in a small deli tucked away from the bustle of Third Street, in New York City.

Our exchange was lively, if not profound. We laughed about the movie that we had seen the night before and disagreed about the meaning behind the text we had just finished for our literature seminar. He told me about the moment when he had taken the drastic step into maturity by becoming Michael and refusing to respond to "Mickey". Had he been twelve or fourteen? He couldn't remember, but he did recall that his mother had cried and said he was growing up too quickly. As we bit into our blueberry blintzes, I told him about the blueberries that my sister and I used to pick when we went to visit our cousins in the country. I recalled that I always finished mine before we got back to the house, and my aunt would warn me that I was going to get a very bad stomachache. Of course, I never did.

As our sweet conversation continued, my eyes glanced across the restaurant, stopping at the small corner booth where an elderly couple sat.Her floral-print dress seemed as faded as the cushion on which she had rested her worn handbag, The top of his head was as shiny as the softboiled egg on which he very slowly nibbled.

She also ate her oatmeal at a slow, almost tedious pace.

But what drew my thoughts to them was their undisturbed silence. It seemed to me that a melancholy emptiness permeated their little corner.

As the exchange between Michael and me fluctuated from laughs to whispers, confessions to assessments, this couple's poignant stillness called to me. How sad, I thought, not to have any thing left to say. Wasn't there any page that they hadn't yet turned in each other's stories? What if that happened to us?

Michael and I paid our small tab and got up to leave the restaurant. As we walked by the corner where the old couple sat, I accidentally dropped my wallet. Bending over to pick it up, I noticed that under the table, each of their free hands was gently cradled in the other's. They had been holding hands all this time!

I stood up and felt humbled by the simple yet profound act of connection I had just been privileged to witness. This man's gentle caress of his wife's tired fingers filled not only what I had previously perceived as an emotionally empty corner, but also my heart. Theirs was not the uncomfortable silence whose threat one always feels just behind the punch line or at the end of an anecdote on the first date. No, theirs was a comfortable, relaxed ease, a gentle love that knew it did not always need words to express itself.

They had probably shared this hour of the morning with each other for a long time, and maybe today wasn't that different from yesterday, but they were at peace with that, and with each other.

Maybe, I thought as Michael and I walked out, it wouldn't be so bad if someday that was us. Maybe, it would be kind of nice.

渴望你的爱

赫尔曼与罗玛·罗森布拉特

1942年冬季的一天,天空昏暗阴冷,寒风刺骨。在纳粹集中营里,天天都是这种日子。自从我和无数犹太人一起被迫离开家园,来到这里以后,每天我就如同行尸走肉一般,活一天是一天,活一小时是一小时。明天,我还能活着吗?今晚,我会不会被带到毒气室呢?

沿着铁丝网,我来回地走着,想暖和一下我瘦弱的身体。我很饿,很久没有吃东西了。每天都有很多人从我们当中消失,幸福的往昔犹如南柯一梦,我也日渐陷入更深的绝望之中。

突然,一个小女孩从铁丝网那边走来。经过我面前时,她停了下来,忧伤的眼睛注视着我,似乎是在说她理解我的感受,但不知道我为什么会在这里。被这个陌生人如此凝视,我感到特别不好意思,我想移开目光,但视线无法从她身上移走。这时,她把手伸进口袋,掏出一个红苹果。噢,我有多久没见过这样的苹果了!她谨慎地左右看了看,然后面带着胜利的微笑,一下子把它抛过铁栅栏。我跑过去将它捡起来,用冻僵得颤抖的手捧着它。在这个充满死亡的世界中,苹果所表达的无疑是生命和关爱。我抬起头来,发现那女孩已经消失在远处了。

第二天,我鬼使神差地在同一时间又来到靠近铁丝网的同一地点。她真的又来了。

21

她再次给我带来了苹果,带着同样甜蜜的笑容把它抛过铁栅栏。这一次我接住了苹果,捧着让她看,她眼里闪烁着光芒。接下来的七个月,我们每天都这样相见。可是有一天,我听到了一个骇人的消息:我们将被押往另一个集中营。

第二天,我见到她时,难过得说不出话来,但又不得不说:"明天,不要给我带苹果了!"我告诉她,"我将被押往另外一个集中营。"在我还能控制住自己的感情时,我转身从铁丝网旁跑开了。我实在不忍心回头。

一晃数月过去了,噩梦依然。但对小姑娘的思念,一直支撑着我度过了那些恐怖、痛苦和无望的日子。噩梦终结,战争结束的这一天终于来临。幸存下来的人获得了自由。我失去了一切珍贵的东西,包括我的家庭。但我仍然惦记着那个小女孩,把对她的记忆一直珍藏在心底。在我移居美国开始新的生活后,她始终激励着我好好活下去。

岁月流逝,转眼到了1957年。我定居美国后,一个朋友想撮合我和他认识的一位女士约会,我勉强答应下来了。她叫罗玛,人很好,跟我一样,也是移民,因此,至少在这一点上,我们有着共同之处。

"战争期间,你在哪儿?"罗玛柔声细语地问道,以移民之间相互问及那段岁月所特有的体贴的方式。

"我在德国的一个集中营。"我答道。

罗玛陷入遐思,似乎想起了某些痛苦而又略带甜蜜的事情。

"你怎么了?"我问道。

"我只是想起了过去的一些事,赫尔曼。"罗玛解释道,声音突然变得无比温柔,"你知道吗?小时候我住在一个集中营附近。那儿有一个男孩,一个小囚犯,很长一段时间,我每天都去看他,我常常给他带苹果。我把苹果扔过铁栅栏去给他,那时他是多么地开心啊。"

罗玛重重地叹了一口气,又接着说:"很难描述当时我们对彼此的感觉——毕竟,那时的我们很小,情况允许时,也只是相互谈上几句而已——但我可以告诉你,里面包含着很多爱。我猜测他可能被杀害了,跟无数人一样。但我实在不愿这么想,所以老想起和他相处的那几个月里他的样子。"

我的心猛烈地跳动起来,我直视着她问:"是不是有一天,那个男孩对你说,明天不要给我带苹果了,我将被押往另外一个集中营'?"

"嗯,是啊。"罗玛颤声应道。

"但是赫尔曼,你怎么会知道这件事呢?"

我握住她的手答道:"罗玛,我正是那个小男孩。"

接下来便是长长的沉默。随着时间面纱的撩开,我们再也不能将眼睛从对方身上移开,我们认出了彼此隐藏于双眼后面的那颗心,我们曾是深深爱恋的朋友,从不曾停止过爱恋、停止过对彼此的思念。

最后,我说:"罗玛,我已经与你分离过一次了,我再也不想与你分开。如今,我重获自由,我希望永远与你在一起。亲爱的,嫁给我好吗?"

罗玛说话时,我再一次从她眼睛里看到了当年的那种光芒,"好,我嫁给你。"

与罗玛重逢至今将近40年了。战争年代,命运让我们首次相聚,同时给了我希望的承诺,如今,我们再次团聚,践行了这一诺言。

1996年的情人节。我带罗玛去参加奥普拉·温弗里的节目,在这个全国性电视节目中,在数百万观众面前,我要向她表示敬意,告诉她我心里一直想说的话:

"亲爱的,在集中营里,当我饥饿难耐时,你给我送来了食物。如今,我仍然饥饿,是那种永远得不到满足的饥饿:我只渴望得到你的爱。"

Hungry for Your Love

Herman and Roma Rosenblat

It is cold, so bitter cold on this dark winter day in 1942. But it is no different from any other day in this Nazi concentration camp. I am almost dead, surviving from day to day, from hour to hour, ever since I was taken from my home and brought here with tens of thousands of other Jews. Will I still be alive tomorrow? Will I be taken to the gas chamber tonight?

Back and forth next to the barbed wire fence trying to keep my emaciated body warm. I am hungry, I have been hungry for long. Each day, as more of us disappear, the happy past seems like a mere dream, and I sink deeper and deeper into despair.

Suddenly, I notice a young girl walking past on the other side of the barbed wire. She stops and looks at me with sad eyes that seem to say that she understands, that she too cannot fathoms why I am here. I want to look away, oddly ashamed for this stranger to see me like this, but I cannot tear my eyes from hers. Then she reaches into her pocket, and pulls out a red apple. Oh, how long has it been since I have seen one! She looks cautiously to the left and to the right and then with smile of triumph quickly throws the apple over the fence. I run to pick it up, holding it in my trembling frozen fingers. In my world of death this apple is an expression of life, of love. I glance up in time to see the girl disappearing into the distance.

The next day I cannot help myself— I am drawn at the same time to that spot near the fence. And again she comes. And again she brings me an apple flinging it over the fence with that same sweet smile. This time I catch it and hold it up for her to see. Her eyes twinkle. For seven months we meet like this. One day I hear frightening news: we're being shipped to another camp.

The next day when I greet her my heart is breaking and I can barely speak as I say what must be said: "Don't bring me an apple tomorrow." I tell her, "I am being sent to another camp." Turning before I lose all my control I run away from the Fence. I cannot bear to look back.

Months pass and the nightmare continues. But the memory of this girl sustains me through the terror, the pain, the hopelessness. And then one day the nightmare is over. The war has ended. Those of us who are still alive are freed. I have lost everything that was precious to me including my family.But I still have the memory of this girl, a memory I carry in my heart and gives me the will to go on as I move to America to start a new life.

Years pass. It is 1957. I am living in New York City. A friend convinces me to go on a blind date with a lady of his. Reluctantly, I agree. But she is nice, this woman named Roma, and like me she is an immigrant so we have at least that in common.

"Where were you during the war?" Roma asks me gently in that delicate way immigrants ask one another questions about those years.

"I was in a concentration camp in Germany." I reply.

Roma gets a faraway look in her eyes, as if she is remembering something painful yet sweet.

"What is it?" I ask.

"I am just thinking about something from my past, Herman," Roma explains in a voice suddenly very soft, "You see, when I was a young girl I lived near a concentration camp. Where was a boy there, a prisoner and for a long while I used to visit him every day. I remember I used to bring him apples. I would throw the apple over the fence and he would be so happy."

Roma sighs heavily and continues, " It is hard to describe how we felt about each other—after all we were young and we only exchanged a few words when we could but I can tellyou there was much love there. I assume he was killed like so many others. But I cannot bear to think that,and so I try to remember him as he was for those months we were given together."

With my heart pounding so loudly, I look directly at Roma and ask,"And did that boy say to you one day 'do not bring me an apple tomorrow.I am being sent to another camp ?"

"Why, yes." Roma responds, her voice trembling.

"But Herman, how on earth could you possibly know that?"

I take her hands in mine and answer, "Because I was that young boy,Roma."

For many moments, there is only silence. We cannot take our eyes from each other, and as the veils of time lift, we recognize the soul behind the eyes, the dear friend we once loved so much, whom we have never stopped loving, whom we have never stopped remembering.

Finally, I speak, "Look, Roma, I was separated from you once, and I don't ever want to be separated from you again. Now I am free, and I want to be together with you forever. Dear, will you marry me?"

I see the same twinkle in her eyes that I used to see as Roma says,"Yes, I will marry you."

Almost forty years have passed since that day when I found nay Roma again. Destiny brought us together the first time during the war to show me a promise of hope, and now it bad reunited us to fulfill that promise.

Valentine's Day, 1996. I bring Roma to the Oprah Winfrey Show to honor her on national television. I want to tell her in front of the millions of the people what I feel in my heart every day:

"Darling, you fed me in the concentration camp when I was hungry.And I am still hungry, for something I will never get enough of : I am only hungry for your love."

奉献

卡连·巴伯

马多克斯小姐进入教堂时经常要穿过市镇草坪的前门，而我们则从后门的停车场进入。每个星期天的早晨，在我们走上通往教堂大厅的通道时，都可以看到马多克斯小姐蹒跚而来，那保龄球木瓶般的腿还一摇一摆的。从远处看，她就像个泥人——穿着一件毫无光泽的毛线外套，戴着一顶遮住耳朵的毛线帽子。

一旦马多克斯小姐上前和我们打招呼时，她那长期不刷的牙齿就会露出来。每次和她打招呼，我都要屏住呼吸。那个时候，我只有24岁，同丈夫戈登一起刚从南卡罗来纳州迁到新泽西州。在南方的时候，我从未闻到过羊毛被汗水浸湿，却又从来没有洗过的味道。

在做礼拜的过程中，戈登和我发现了一件令人极为不快的事，那就是当教堂里热得让马多克斯小姐浑身冒汗时，她身上所散发出来的那股味道就更难闻了。她把外套的扣子从头到尾系得紧紧的，也从来不摘帽子。很快，我们就特别小心地移到和她相隔几排的座位上了。

在这里我们还认识了另外一些年轻夫妇，他们都是由于企业搬迁而从不同的地区来到这里的。我一直忙于和他们交谈，所以至今也未曾问过马多克斯小姐来自哪里。我猜测，她就是在这片绿地上长大的，就像个冬季的萝卜。

有几个月的时间，我们和马多克斯小姐之间仅仅是在通道中勉强问个好而已。接着，我怀了我们的第一个孩子，这个消息传到了马多克斯小姐那里。在随后的一个礼拜天，她就像我们的一个长期失去联系的亲戚似的，满心欢喜地走向我，问道："小妈妈今天感觉如何呀？"

我试着回答她，可是话总是被堵在喉咙里说不出来，我只是淡淡地笑了一下。时间一个月一个月地过去，我们与她之间不仅仅是礼貌的点头了。我的妊娠仿佛一块磁铁，把马多克斯小姐吸引了过来。每当她看到我，都会走过来用她那出汗的手摸摸我隆起的腹部，然后摇摇头说道："我们的小妈妈呀!"我从来不知道该怎样回应她。我容忍她，却从来没有鼓励过她。她所谈及的有关婴儿的唠叨有些怪异。她从未说起过她所熟悉的婴儿，抑或有关她自己的儿孙，或者外甥、外甥女有趣的事情。出于某些原因，她对我怀上孩子显得极为高兴，并且不知道为什么，她甚至了解我的心思。

预产期渐渐来临，马多克斯小姐对我的妊娠也更加关心，总想弄清楚我是否还怀着孩子。我的恐惧与日俱增，她究竟想从我这里得到什么呢?

在我的预产期来临前的一个星期天，我终于知道了答案。那一天，马多克斯小姐捧着一只粗糙的衬衣盒子出现在教堂里。那个盒子太小了，以至于盒子里装的东西都鼓了出来。她一看到我，就大笑起来，面孔仿佛都要被她的笑撑裂了似的。她冲我叫道："喂，我有件东西给你。"

马克多斯小姐把盒子塞到我的手里，盒子裂开了，露出一条钩边的毯子。马多克斯小姐将那条用粗纱线钩成的婴儿毯展开——那是一大块有着淡绿色花边的白色钩编毯。这块毯子非常厚实，编织得特别密实，而且是按照婴儿的全身尺寸织成的，足以把婴儿床垫盖住。它不单单是一件钩编杰作，还是一件在纱线短缺的情况下完成的杰作。从它不规则的边沿可以看出，每一束纱线都是在她手头存够一两美元的时候才买来的，并且这期间的时间间隔都很长。

在我凝望着马多克斯小姐黯淡无光的眼睛时，我看到的是纯粹的快乐。几个月以来她那热情的唠叨刹时间有了解释。马多克斯小姐所知道的唯一一件事就是婴儿需要一条毯子，而且很显然，钩编艺术是她这一生最大的才能。每当她用手丈量我的腹围时，她就明白那条非凡的毯子她还需要钩多长才能完成。她的快乐不只是来自于将要出生的婴儿，更多的是有机会做出奉献。

一瞬间，我知道我得到的是令我感到羞愧的馈赠。"真好看!"我结结巴巴地说，一边用手拍着她那柔软的肩膀，"等孩子出生后，你会是这个地方第一个抱他的人。"

她对着我微笑，把双臂交叉在胸前，做出一个抱孩子的姿势。尽管她还是穿着那件旧毛线外套，还是那样蹒跚地走着，然而这一次我却觉得有所不同，我只能把这种感觉叫作爱。

Outgiven

Karen Barber

Miss Maddox always entered our church from the front door that opened onto the town green. We came through the back door from the parking lot. Every Sunday morning as we walked up the aisle we could see Miss Maddox waddling down it on her bowling-pin legs. From a distance she looked like a clay figure in a dingy wool coat and a knit hat pulled down over her ears.

When Miss Maddox got close enough to greet us, the long-term neglect of her teeth showed. It was during the greeting that I held my breath. When I was only 24 years old, my husband, Gordon, and I had just moved from South Carolina to New Jersey. In the South I hadn't been exposed to the smell of wool that had been sweat in and never washed.

During worship, Gordon and I made the unhappy discovery that the smell sharpened as Miss Maddox warmed up to a swelter in the heated sanctuary, her coat firmly buttoned to the top, and her hat never removed. We soon took extra care to seat ourselves several rows away from her.

Here we found other young couples who had been displaced from different regions by corporate moves. I was so busy with them that I never asked Miss Maddox where she came

29

from. I assumed she had grown up right on the green, like a winter turnip.

For several months that was all there was between Miss Maddox and us, a forced greeting in mid aisle. Then I became pregnant with our first child. The news got around to Miss Maddox and the very next Sunday she came for me like a long-lost relative, gushing with delight, "How's the little mother today?"

I tried to answer, but the words got stuck in my throat and I simply smiled weakly. As the months wore on, there was no going back to our polite nods. My pregnancy was like a magnet that drew Miss Maddox to me. Every time she saw me she came over and touched my swollen stomach with her sweaty hand. Then she bobbed her head and said, "Here's the little mother." I never knew how to respond. I tolerated her, but never encouraged her. There was something odd in her babbling about babies. She never made references to babies she had known, or told cute stories about children, grandchildren or even a niece or nephew. For some reason she was overjoyed that I was having a baby and that she, in some tenuous way, knew me.

As my due date drew near, Miss Maddox became more intent on making sure I was still pregnant. My dread began to rise. What was it she wanted from me?

My answer came the Sunday before my due date when Miss Maddox turned up at church with a flimsy shirt box that was too small for its bulging contents. When she saw me she burst into a smile big enough to crack her face. "Yoohoo," she called, "I've got something for you."

She shoved the box into my hands and it spilled open, revealing a piece of crochet. Miss Maddox unfolded a baby blanket made of thick yarn, a block of white surrounded by an aqua border. It was a heavy, fullbodied yarn executed in an airtight stitch, big enough to cover a crib mattress. Not only was it a master piece, but it was also done despite meager resources. The irregular border indicated that over a long period of time each skein of yarn had been bought and hoarded whenever a dollar or two was available.

As I stared into Miss Maddox's faded eyes, I read pure delight. Suddenly her months of effusive babbling made sense. The only thing Miss Maddox knew about babies was that they needed blankets, and crochet was clearly her big talent in life. Every time she had sized up my stomach, she had been gauging how much longer she had to finish the remarkable blanket. Her joy had not been so much about the baby as it was about the opportunity to give.

At that moment I knew that I had been outgiven. "It's lovely." I stammered, putting Miss Maddox's soft shoulder. "When the baby comes, you'll be the first one who is here to hold it."

She beamed at me and clasped her arms in a cradling motion across her chest. Although she was still swaddled in that old wool coat, this time I sensed something different. I can only call it love.

生活的意义

阿尔弗雷德·阿德勒

假如我们问:"什么是生活的意义?"人们可能不知道怎么回答。大多数时候,人们不会把自己陷入这个问题的困扰中,或者试图解释清楚。其实这个问题就像人类自身一样古老。在我们这个时代,年轻人——老人也同样如此——有时会问:"我为什么而活?什么是生活的意义?"可以肯定的是,只有在遇到挫折的时候,他们才会提出这种问题来。如果生活万事顺利,不需面对困难的考验,他们永远不会问这样的问题。但是,无法避免地,每个人都会在他的行动中反映了这些问题和答案。如果我们不听任何人的话语,只留意于每个人的行动,那么我们会看到:他们在阐释自己独特的"生活的意义"。他的观点、看法、行为、表达方式、癖好、雄心、习性和性格特点,都和生活的意义一致。每个人的举止、表现都是他依赖于生活中的某种阐释。他的所有行动,是对这个世界和他自己看法的体现,结论是:"这就是我,那就是宇宙。"这就是他给自己和生活的意义。

世上有各式各样的人,所以生活的意义也多种多样,或许每个意义在某种程度上都是错误的。没有人知道生活的意义到底是什么,所以谁也不能全盘否定任何一种对生活意义的解释。所有的意义都在两个极端中间变化不定。但是在这种变化中,我们却能辨别出什么是好的,什么是不好的;哪些错误尚小,哪些错误大些。我们还能看到,这些优良的解释有什么共同之处,而那些相对差的解释欠缺之处又是什么。我们可以从这个事实中得出一个共同的标准,一个普遍的生活的意义,这样它就能使我们解释后来与人类有关的所有真实的意义,这种真实是对人类的目的和意图的真实。此外,再没有别的真实。即便有另一种真实存在,它也不被我们所关注,我们不了解它,那么它也就没有存在的意义。

个体心理学研究发现,人类的所有问题可以分为三个部分,即:职业、社交和性。一个人对这三个问题的反映实际上便是他对生活意义的阐释。我们来假设一下,例如一个人的爱情生活不如意或者就没有爱情,不努力工作,朋友没有几个,与人交往也令他感到头疼。他的生活充满的是自我约束和限制,由此我们可以得出:他把生存看作是一件艰难而危险的事,很少有机会,而失败又太多。他狭窄的生活圈子恰恰表达了他的观点:"生活的意义就是保护自己免受伤害,封闭自己,逃避伤害。"

我们从另一个方面来说,假设一个人他有完美甜蜜的爱情生活,工作卓有成绩,朋友众多,交际很广,收益颇丰,那么我们就可以断言,这样一个人,生活具有创造性,有很多机遇,并且没有什么不可跨越的障碍。面临生活中的各种困难,他的勇气可以概括为:"对他人产生兴趣,使自己成为整体中的一部分,用自己的力量为人类的幸福做一份贡献,这就是生活的意义。"

The Meaning of Life

Alfred

If we asked someone, "What is the meaning of life?" he would probably be unable to answer. For the most part, people do not trouble themselves with the question or try to formulate any answers. It is true that the question is as old as humanity itself and that in our own time young people—and older people too will sometimes demand, "But what is life for? What does life mean?" It is fair to say, however, that they only ask these questions when they have suffered some sort of setback. So long as life is smooth sailing and they are not confronting difficult tests, the question is never put into words. It is, rather, in his actions that each person inevitably poses these questions and answers them. If we closed our ears to words and concentrated on observing actions, we would find that each person has formulated his own individual "meaning of life,"and that all his opinions, attitudes, movements, expressions, mannerisms, ambitions, habits, and character traits are in a aecordance with this meaning. Each person behaves as if he could rely upon a certain interpretation of life. In all his actions, there is an implicit summing up of the world and of himself. The verdict, "I am like this and the universe is like that." has a meaning given to himself,and a meaning ascribed to life.

There are as many meanings ascribed to life as there are human beings, and perhaps, each meaning is mistaken to some extent. No one knows the absolute meaning of life, and thus any interpretation that is at all serviceable cannot be called ahsolutely wrong. All meananings are variations between these two limits. Among these variations, however, we can distinguish some that work well and some that are less effective; some where the mistake is small and some where it is large. We can discover what it is that the better interpretations have in common and what it is that the less satisfactory interpretations lack. We can derive from these a common measure of the truth, a common meaning, which enables us to decipher reality insofar as it concerns humankind. Again, we must bear in mind that true means true for humankind, true for the purpose and aims of human beings. There is no other truth than this. Even if another truth existed, it would not concern us. We could never know it; it would be meaningless.

Individual psychology has found that all human problems can be grouped under three main headings: occupational, social, and sexual. It is in his response to these three problems that every individual human being unfailingly reveals his own personal interpretation of the meaning of life. Suppose, for example, we consider a person whose love life is unsatisfactory or nonexistent, who fails to exert himself in his profession, who has few friends,and who finds contact with his fellow human beings painful. From the self-imposed limits and restrictions in his life, we may conclude that he sees being alive as a difficult and dangerous thing, entailing few opportunities and many failures. His narrow field of action can be construed as expressing the opinion: "Life means protecting myself against harm, barricading myself in, and escaping unscathed."

Suppose, on the other hand, we consider a person who has a love relationship that is an intimate and full cooperation, whose work results in useful achievements, who has lots of friends, and whose contacts with people are wide-ranging and fruitful. We may conclude that such a person sees life as a creative task, offering many opportunities and no irreversible setbacks. His courage in confronting all the problems of life is to be construed as saying: "Life means being interested in people, being part of the whole, and contributing my share the welare of humankind."

论门

C.D莫利

人生最有意义的动作就是开门和关门。门内将会是怎样的神秘景象啊! 没有人知道当他推开一扇门,等待他的是什么。即便是最熟悉的房间,时钟滴答滴答地走着,壁炉的红色火焰在暮色中闪烁,也有可能会发生令人吃惊的事。水管工人可能已经拜访过(就在你不在家的时候),把坏了的水龙头修好了。厨娘没准儿正烦恼郁闷,想请你准予她离开。有头脑的人总是抱着谦虚接受的态度推开他面前的那扇门。

哪个人没有在某间接待室坐过,双眼紧盯着那扇无法预测的意味深长的门?或许你要应聘,或许你迫切地想要做成一笔生意。你看着机密速记员出来进去,毫不在意地旋转着那扇关系着你命运铰链的神秘大门。然后,那个年轻女人说:"克雷伯里先生现在想要见你。"就在你抓住门柄的时候,一个念头一闪而过:"当我再次推开这扇门的时候,将会发生什么呢?"

门的种类有许多。有旅馆、商店和公共建筑的十字形旋转门,这是轻快且繁忙的现代生活方式的象征。你能想象得出约翰·弥尔顿或威廉·佩恩从一扇旋转门匆匆走过吗?还有一些古怪而倾斜的小门,依然在变了质的酒吧外摇摆,并且只有膝盖到肩膀这么高。还有活板门、滑门、双折门、舞台门、监狱门和玻璃门。但是一扇门的象征和神秘之处就体现在它的隐蔽性上。玻璃门仅仅是一扇窗,根本就不是门。门的意义就是把门内的一切隐藏起来,让你的心处于焦虑之中。

与此同时,开门的方式也有许多。其中一种是用胳膊肘轻快地一推,比如服务员端着你的晚餐,打开厨房的门时。一个不开心的书商或小贩拉开门时,是犹豫和存有戒心的。上流社会细心谨慎的男仆会退步而出为重要人物敞开栎木大门。以及富有同情心的牙医女助手轻轻推开手术室的门,然后什么也不说,暗示你医生已经准备好了。此外还有,大清早,护士轻快且忽然地推开门进来,喊道:"是个男孩!"门意味着隐私、退却、心灵

智慧英文励志篇

退避到幸福的平静或伤心的秘密挣扎。一个房间没有门就不算房间,只是一个走廊。一个人待在一扇关闭着的门后,不管是在哪儿,他都能让自己感觉像是在家里。人的思维在关闭着的门后状态最为活跃。人不是马,要成群地在一起。狗知道门所带来的意义和苦恼。你是否留意到一只小狗对一扇关着的门充满向往?这象征着人类的生活。

开门的动作是神秘的,充满着一些不可预知的滋味,投进新的一瞬的感觉,一种人类冗长繁乱的新形式。它显示出最高境界的快乐:团圆、和解、久别重逢的恋人的欣喜。即使是悲哀,打开的门也会给你以安慰,它改变并重组人的力量。可是,关门是骇人的,它彰显的是结束。每一扇门的关闭都意味着一些事情的终结。关门也有着不同程度的悲哀。"砰"地把门关上是虚弱的象征,轻轻把门带上往往是一生中最悲壮的动作。每个人都明白,苦痛随后即到。就在关上门后,深爱的人虽近在咫尺,仍能听到声音,却已渐渐远去。

开门和关门是严肃且匆匆而逝的一生中的一部分。生命不会停滞不前,弃我们于不顾。我们满怀希望不断地开门,却常常带着失望关门。人的一生不过一管烟的长度,我们就像烟灰一样被命运击倒。

关上一扇门是不可避免的。它猛然折断心脏的血管,重新打开,再放回去,也是徒劳。皮尼罗让波拉·坦克瑞说:"未来只是过去通过另一道门进来了。"这简直是谬论。唉,没有其他的门! 当这扇门关上了,它就永远地闭上了。那消失了脉搏的时间,再也没有其他的入口。"手指运动,在纸上写下字迹……"

我们都会遇到这么一类关门。这种门是静静关上的,打破寂静的只有弹簧锁的咔哒声。但愿当时他们所想的不是我们曾经做过的坏事,而是我们尚未完成的正事。那么,他们将会走出去……

On Doors

C.D.Moley

The opening and closing of doors are the most significant actions of man's life.What a mystery lies in doors!

No man knows what awaits him when he opens a door. Even the most familiar room, where the clock ticks and the hearth glows red at dusk, may harbor surprise. The plumber may actually have called (while you were out) and ixed that leaking faucet. The cook may have had a fit of the vapors1 and demanded her passports. The wise man opens his front door with humility and a spirit of acceptance.

Which one of us has not sat in some anteroom and watched the inscrutable panels of a door that was full of meaning? Perhaps you were waiting to apply for a job; perhaps you had some "deal" you were ambitious to put over. You watched the confidential stenographer flit in and out, carelessly turning that mystic portal which, to you, revolved on hinges of fate.And then the young woman said, "Mr. Cranberry will see you now."As you grasped the knob the thought flashed, "When I open this door again, what will have happened?"

There are many kinds of doors. Revolving doors for hotels, shops, and public buildings that are typical of the brisk, bustling ways of modern life. Can you imagine John Milton or William Penn skipping through a revolving door? Then there are the curious little slanted doors that still swing outside denatured bar−rooms and extend only from shoulder to knee. There are trapdoors, sliding doors, double doors, stage doors, prison doors, glass doors. But the symbol and mystery of a door resides in its quality of concealment. A glass door is not a door at all, but a window. The meaning of a door is to hide what lies inside; to keep the heart in suspense.

Also, there are many ways of opening doors. There is a cheery push of an elbow with which the waiter shoves open the kitchen door when he bears in your tray of supper. There is the suspicious and tentative withdrawal of a door before the unhappy book agent or peddler. There is the genteel and carefully modulated recession with which footmen swing wide the oaken barriers of the great. There is the sympathetic and awful silence of me dentist's maid who opens the door into the operating room, and, without speaking, implies that the doctor is ready for you. There is the brisk cataclysmic opening of a door when the nurses come in, very early in the morning—"It's a boy! "

Doors are at the symbol of privacy, of retreat, of the mind's escape into blissful quietude or sad secret struggle. A room without doors is not a room, but a hallway. No matter where he is, a man can make himself at home behind a closed door. The mind works best behind closed doors. Men are not horses to be herded together. Dogs know the meaning and anguish of doors. Have you ever noticed a puppy yearning at a shut portal? It is a symbol of human life.

The opening of doors is a mystic act: it has in some flavor of the unknown, some sense of moving into a new moment, a new pattern of human rigmarole. It includes the highest glimpses of mortal gladness: reunions, reconciliations, the bliss of lovers long parted. Even in sadness, the opening of a door may bring relief: it changes and redistributes human forces. But the closing of doors is far more terrible. It is a confession of finality. Every door closed brings something to an end. And there are degrees of sadness in the closing of doors.A door slammed is a confession of weakness. A door gently shut is often the most tragic gesture in life. Every one knows the seizure of anguish that comes just after the closing of a door, when the loved one is still near, with sound of voice, and yet already far away.

The opening and closing of doors is a part of the stern fluency of life. Life will not stay still and let us alone. We are continually opening doors with hope, closing them with despair. Life lasts not much longer than a pipe of tobacco, and destiny knocks us out like ashes.

The closing of a door is irrevocable. It snaps the back-thread of the heart. It is no avail to reopen, to go back. Pinero spoke nonsense when he made Paula Tanqueray say, "The future is only the past entered through another gate." Alas, there is no other gate.When the door is shut, it is shut forever. There is no other entrance to that vanished pulse of time. "The moving finger writes, and have writ..."

There is a certain kind of door shutting that will come to us all. The kind of door shutting that is done very quietly, with the sharp click of the latch to break the stillness. They will think then, one hopes, of our unfulfilled decencies rather than of our pluperfected misdemeanors. Then they will go out and...

一个男孩的使命

佚名

1945年，一个12岁的男孩在一家商店橱窗里看到一样令他心动的东西。但是5美元——远不是鲁本·厄尔能付得起的。5美元几乎够买全家一周的食物呢。

鲁本不能向父亲要钱。马克·厄尔的每一分钱都是靠在加拿大纽芬兰的罗伯茨湾捕鱼挣来的。鲁本的母亲多拉，为了不让5个孩子冻着饿着，差不多是一个钱当两个钱用。

尽管如此，鲁本还是推开商店那扇久经风雨的门走了进去。他穿着面粉袋改做的衬衫和洗得褪了色的裤子，站得笔直，丝毫不觉困窘。他告诉了店主他想要的东西，又加上一句："可我现在还没有钱买它。您能为我预留一段时间吗？"

"我尽量吧，"店主微笑着说，"这儿的人买起东西来，一般不会花那么大一笔钱的。一时半会儿卖不出去。"

鲁本很有礼貌地碰了碰他的旧帽沿儿，走出店外。阳光下清新的微风吹得罗伯茨湾的海水泛起阵阵涟漪。鲁本迈着大步，下定决心：他要凑齐那5美元，而且不告诉任何人。

听到街边传来的铁锤声，鲁本有了主意。

他循声跑过去，来到一处建筑工地。罗伯茨湾的人喜欢自己建房，用的钉子是从本地一家工厂买的，都用麻袋来装。有时干活时，忙乱中麻袋就被随手丢弃，而鲁本知道他可以5美分一条把麻袋再卖给工厂。

那天，他找到了两条麻袋，拿到杂乱的木材厂，卖给为钉子装袋的人。

两公里的路程他是一路跑着回的家，手里紧紧攥着两个5分硬币。

他家旁边有个颇有年头的谷仓，里面圈着家里的山羊和鸡。鲁本在那里找到一个生锈的装苏打的铁罐，把两枚硬币放了进去。然后，他爬上谷仓的阁楼，把铁罐藏在一堆散发着甜香味的干草下面。

晚饭时分，鲁本跨进家门。父亲正坐在厨房大餐桌旁摆弄渔网，母亲多拉在灶台边忙碌着，准备开饭。鲁本就在桌边坐下了。

他看着妈妈，笑了。窗户透进的夕阳余晖将她棕褐的披肩发染成了金色。苗条、美丽的母亲是这个家的中心，她像胶水一样使这个家紧紧连结在一起。

母亲的家务活永远也没个完。用老式的"胜家"缝纫机为一家人缝缝补补；要做饭、烤面包；要照料菜园；要挤羊奶；还要在洗衣板上搓洗脏衣服。可母亲是快乐的，全家人的幸福、健康在她心中是最重要的。

每天放学，做完家务事后，鲁本就在镇上搜寻装钉子的麻袋。只有两间教室的学校开始放暑假的那天，没人能比鲁本更高兴了。现在他有更多时间去完成他的使命。

整整一个夏天，鲁本除了干家务——给菜园锄草、浇水、砍柴和打水外，始终进行着他的秘密任务。

转眼菜园里该采收了，蔬菜被装罐腌制后储藏，学校也开学了。再不久，树叶飘零，海湾吹起阵阵寒风。鲁本在街头徘徊，努力寻找着被他视为宝物的麻袋。

他经常是饥寒交迫，疲惫不堪，但是一想到商店橱窗里的那样东西，他就又有劲儿坚持下去了。有时妈妈会问："鲁本，你上哪儿啦？我们等你吃饭呢！"

"玩去啦，妈妈。对不起。"

这时候，多拉总会瞧着他的脸，无奈地摇摇头，心想：男孩就是男孩。

春天终于来了，带来片片绿意，鲁本的精神也随之振奋。是时候了！他跑到谷仓，爬上草垛，打开铁罐，倒出所有硬币清点起来。

他又数一遍，还差20美分。镇上哪儿还会有丢弃的麻袋吗？他必须在今天结束之前再找4条去卖掉。

鲁本沿着沃特街走着。

鲁本赶到工厂，厂房的影子已被夕阳拉得很长了。收购麻袋的人正要锁门。

"先生！请先不要关门。"

那人转过身来,看到了脏兮兮、汗涔涔的鲁本。

"明天再来吧,孩子。"

"求您了,先生。我必须现在把麻袋卖掉——求您啦。"那人感觉到鲁本的声音在颤抖,知道他快要哭了。

"你为什么这么急着要这点儿钱?"

"这是秘密。"

那人接过麻袋,手伸进口袋,掏出4个硬币放在鲁本手里。鲁本轻轻说了声"谢谢"就往家跑。

接着,他紧紧搂着铁罐,直奔那家商店。

"我有那笔钱啦!"他一本正经地告诉店主。

店主走向橱窗,取出鲁本梦寐以求的东西。

他掸去灰尘,用牛皮纸把它小心包好,然后把这个小包放到鲁本手上。

鲁本一路狂奔到家,冲进前门。妈妈正在厨房擦洗灶台。"瞧,妈妈!瞧!"鲁本一边跑向她一边大叫着。他把一个小盒子放在她因劳作而变得粗糙的手上。

为了不损坏包装纸,她小心翼翼地把它拆开。一个蓝色天鹅绒的首饰盒映入眼帘。多拉打开盒盖,泪水顿时模糊了她的双眼。

在一个小巧的心状胸针上刻着金字:母亲。

那是1946年的母亲节。

多拉从来没有收到过这样的礼物,除了结婚戒指外她没有华丽的衣服。此时,她无法言语,会心地笑着,用双臂紧紧地拥住了儿子。

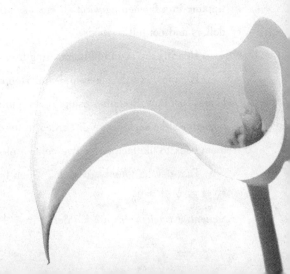

A Boy With A Mission

Anonymous

In 1945, a 12–year–old boy saw something in a shop window that set his heart racing. But the price—five dollars—was far beyond Reuben Earle's means. Five dollars would buy almost a week's groceries for his family.

Reuben couldn't ask his father for the money. Everything Mark Earle made through fishing in Bay Roberts, Newfoundland, and Cana da. Reuben's mother, Dora, stretched like elastic to feed and clothetheir five children.

Nevertheless, he opened the shop's weathered door and went inside. Standing proud and straight in his flour–sack shirt and washed–out trousers, he told the shopkeeper what he wanted,adding, "But I don't have the money right now. Can you please hold it for me for some time? "

"I'll try," the shopkeeper smiled, "Folks around here don't usually have that kind of money to spend on things. It should keep for a while."

Reuben respectfully touched his worn cap and walked out into the sunlight with the bay tippling in a freshening wind. There was purpose in his loping stride. He would raise the five dollars and not tell anybody.

Hearing the sound of hammering from a side street, Reuben had an idea.

He ran towards the sound and stopped at a construction site. People built their own homes in Bay Roberts, using nails purchased in Hessian sacks from a local factory. Sometimes the sacks were discarded in the flurry of building, and Reuben knew he could sell them back to the factory for five cents a piece.

That day he found two sacks, which he took to the rambling wooden factory and sold to

智慧英文励志篇

the man in charge of packing nails.

The boy's hand tightly clutched the five-cent pieces as he ran the two kilometers home.

Near his house stood the ancient barn that housed the family's goats and chickens. Reuben found a rusty soda tin and dropped his coins inside. Then he climbed into the loft of the barn and hid the tin beneath a pile of sweet smelling hay.

It was dinnertime when Reuben got home. His father sat at the big kitchen table, working on fishing net. Dora was at the kitchen stove, ready to serve dinner as Reuben took his place at the table.

He looked at his mother and smiled. Sunlight from the window gilded her shoulder-length blonde hair. Slim and beautiful, she was the center of the home, the glue that held it together.

Her chores were never-ending. Sewing clothes for her family on the old Singer treadle machine, cooking meals and baking bread, planting and tending a vegetable garden, milking the goats and scrubbing soiled clothes on a washboard. But she was happy. Her family and their well-being were her highest priority.

Every day after chores and school, Reuben scoured the town, collecting the Hessians nail bags. On the day the two-room school closed for the summer, no student was more delighted than Reuben. Now he would have more time for his mission.

All summer long, despite chores at home weeding and watering the garden, cutting wood and fetching water—Reuben kept to his secret task.

Then all too soon the garden was harvested, the vegetables canned and stored, and the school reopened. Soon the leaves fell and the winds blew cold and gusty from the bay. Reuben wandered the streets, diligently searching for his hessian treasures.

Often he was cold, tired and hungry, but the thought of the object in the shop window sustained him. Sometimes his mother would ask:"Reuben, where were you? We were waiting for you to have dinner."

"Playing, Mum. Sorry."

Dora would look at his face and shake her head. Boys.

Finally spring burst into glorious green and Reuben's spirits erupted. The time had come ! He ran into the barn, climbed to the hayloft and uncovered the tin can. He poured the coins out and began to count.

Then he counted again. He needed 20 cents more. Could there be any sacks left any where in town? He had to find four and sell them before the day ended.

Reuben ran down Water Street.

The shadows were lengthening when Reuben arrived at the factory. The sack buyer was about to lock up.

"Mister! Please don't close up yet."

The man turned and saw Reuben, dirty and sweat stained.

"Come back tomorrow, boy."

"Please, Mister. I have to sell the sacks now—please." The man heard a tremor in Reuben's voice and could tell he was close to tears.

"Why do you need this money so badly? "

"It's a secret."

The man took the sacks, reached into his pocket and put four coins in Reuben's hand. Reuben murmured a thank you and ran home.

Then, clutching the tin can, he headed for the shop.

"I have the money." he solemnly told the owner.

The man went to the window and retrieved Reuben's treasure.

He wiped the dust off and gently wrapped it in brown paper, Then he placed the parcel in Reuben's hands.

Racing home, Reuben burst through the front door. His mother was scrubbing the kitchen stove. "Here, Mum! Here! " Reuben exclaimed as he ran to her side. He placed a small box in her work roughened hand.

She unwrapped it carefully, to save the paper. A blue-velvet jewel box appeared. Dora lifted the lid, tears beginning to blur her vision.

In gold lettering on a small, almond-shaped brooch was the word Mother.

It was Mother's Day, 1946.

Dora had never received such a gift; she had no finery except her wedding ring. Speechless, she smiled radiantly and gathered her son into her arms.

两幅母亲肖像前

佚名

我深爱这名美丽少女的
画像,她是我的母亲,绘制于多年前
当时她的前额白皙无瑕
如同威尼斯玻璃般闪亮,没有一丝阴影
在她双眸中。但另一幅肖像显出
深深的纹痕布满她皎白大理石般平滑的前额
她少女时的那首玫瑰情诗
曾在她婚礼中被咏唱,如今已经远去。
此时我心悲伤:比较这两幅肖像,一幅显得
神情愉悦,另一幅显得心事重重:
一幅如同朝阳初升——另一幅则如迎面而来的阴郁
黑夜。然而我的反应却显得非比寻常,
因为当我看着她失去光泽的双唇,我心
发出微笑,但看着那名微笑的少女
我的泪竟开始涌出。

Before Two Portraits Of My Mother

Anonymous

I love the beautiful young girl of this

Portrait of my mother, painted years ago

When her forehead was white, and there was no

Shadow in the dazzling Venetian glass

of her gaze. But this other likeness shows

The deep trenches across her forehead's white

Marble. The rose poem of her youth that

Her marriage sang is far behind. Here is

My sadness: I compare these portraits, one

Of a joy-radiant brow, the other care-heavy:

sunrise—and the thick coming on

Of night. And yet how strange my ways appear,

For when I look at these faded lips my heart

Smiles, but at the smiling girl my tears start.

男孩和苹果树

佚名

很久很久以前,有一棵又高又大的苹果树。一个小男孩,天天到树下来。他爬上去摘苹果吃,在树荫下睡觉。他爱苹果树,苹果树也爱和他一起玩耍。

后来,小男孩长大了,不再天天来玩耍。一天他又来到树下,很伤心的样子。苹果树要和他一起玩,男孩说"不行,我不小了,不能再和你玩。我想要玩具,可是没钱买。"苹果树说:"很遗憾,我也没钱,不过,把我所有的果子摘下来卖掉,你不就有钱了?"男孩高兴极了,他摘下所有的苹果,高高兴兴地走了。然后,男孩好久都没有来,苹果树很伤心。

有一天,男孩终于来了,树兴奋地邀他"来和我玩吧。"男孩说:"不行,我没有时间,我要替家里干活呢。我们需要一幢房子,你能帮忙吗?""我没有房子,"苹果树说,"不过你可以把我的树枝统统砍下来,拿去盖房子。"于是男孩砍下所有的树枝,高高兴兴地运走去盖房子。看到男孩高兴,树好快乐。从此,男孩又不来了。树再次陷入孤单和悲伤之中。

一年夏天,男孩回来了,树太快乐了:"来呀!孩子,来和我玩呀。"男孩却说:"我心情不好,一天天老了,我要扬帆出海,轻松一下,你能给我一艘船吗?"苹果树说:"把我的树干砍去,拿去做船吧!"于是男孩砍下了她的树干,造了条船,然后驾船走了,很久都没有回来。树好快乐……但不是真的。

许多年过去,男孩终于回来,苹果树说:"对不起,孩子。我已经没有东西可以给你了,我的苹果没了。"

男孩说:"我的牙都掉了,吃不了苹果了。"

苹果树又说:"我再没有树干,让你爬上来了。"

男孩说:"我太老了,爬不动了。"

"我再也没有什么给得出手了……只剩下枯死的老根。"树流着泪说。

男孩说:"这么多年过去了,现在我感到累了。什么也不想要,只要一个休息的地方。"

"好啊!老根是最适合坐下来休息的。来啊,坐下来和我一起休息吧!"男孩坐下来,苹果树高兴得流下了眼泪……

A Boy And A Tree

Anonymous

A long time ago, there was a huge apple tree. A little boy loved to come and lay around it every day.He climbed to the tree top, ate the apples, and took a nap under the shadow... He loved the tree and the tree loved to play with him.

Time went by...The little boy had grown up and he no longer played around the tree every day. One day, the boy came back to the tree and he looked sad. "Come and play with me." the tree asked the boy. "I am no longer a kid; I don't play around trees anymore." The boy replied, "I want toys. I need money to buy them." "Sorry, I don't have money, but you can pick all all my apples and sell them. So,you will have money." The boy was so excited. He grabbed all the apples on the tree and left happily. The boy never came back after he picked the apples. The tree was sad.

One day, the boy returned and the tree was so excited."Come and play with me." the tree said. "I don't have time to play. I have to work for my family. We need a house for shelter. Can you help me? "

"Sorry, I don't have a house. But you can chop offmy branches to build your house." So the boy cut all the branches offthe tree and left happily. The tree was glad to see him happy but the boy never came back since then. The tree was again lonely and sad.

One hot summer day, the boy returned and the tree was delighted.

"Come and play with me! " the tree said. "I am sad and getting old. I want to go sailing to relax myself. Can you give me a boat? Use my trunk to build your boat. You can sail far away and be happy." So the boy cut the tree trunk to make a boat. He went sailing and never showed up for a long time. The tree was happy, but it was not true.

Finally, the boy returned after he left for so many years. "Sorry, my boy. But I don't have anything for you anymore. No more apples for you..." the tree said.

"I don't have teeth to bite," the boy replied.

"No more trunk for you to climb on."

"I am too old for that now." the boy said.

"I really can't give you anything... the only thing left is my dying roots." the tree said with tears.

"I don't need much now, just a place to rest. I am tired after all these years." The boy replied.

"Good! Old tree roots are the best place to lean on and rest Come, Come sit down with me and rest." The boy sat down and the tree was glad and smiled with tears...

为成功冒险

佚名

一次网球比赛中，莫尼卡·塞莱斯与吉娜·加莉森相遇。随着比赛的进行，塞莱斯清楚地意识到她最大的敌人不是加莉森，而是她自己。

塞莱斯赛后说道："比赛咬得很紧。我总是选择安全的打法。即使是面对加莉森的第二发球，我也不敢主动进攻……"

而加莉森可不想四平八稳。"我对自己说：一定要竭尽全力……假如我输了，至少我知道我已经尽了最大努力。"结果，加莉森占先、夺得局点、盘点、赛点——最后获胜。

你可以问问自己：自己为成功冒足险了吗？

Risk to Succeed

Anonymous

During one tennis match, Monica Seles faced Zina Garrison. As the march proceeded, it became clear that Seles greatest enemy was not Garrison but herself.

Said Seles afterward, "The match was so close. I was going for the safe shorts. Even on Zina's second serve I was scared to hit the ball... "

Garrison, on the other hand, didn't play for safe. "I just told myself to go for it... if I missed, at least I'd know that this time I went for it. "Advantage, game, set and match to Garrison.

You may ask yourself: do you risk enough to succeed?

要学会如何学习

佚名

你有没有想过孩子们为什么要上学？你很可能会说孩子们上学是为了学习本国语和外国语，还有算术、地理、几何、历史、自然科学以及其他学科。这显然没错，但他们为什么要学习这些科目呢？他们在学校学到的就是这些吗？

我们送孩子上学是为他们将来长大成人后能独立生活作准备。他们学习本国语是为了能够明确地告诉别人自己的所求和所知，并且能够理解别人的话语。他们学习外国语是为了能从外国人的著作和言谈中有所获益，并让其他国家的人们理解自己的意图。通过学习算术，他们可以测量和计算日常生活中的事物；通过学习地理，他们可以了解周围的世界；通过学习历史，他们能够了解每天交往的人。他们在学校里学到的所有知识几乎都能在日常生活中得到实际应用，但这难道是他们上学的惟一理由吗？

当然不是。教育的目的不仅仅局限于明理识事。我们上学的首要目的是要学会如何学习；这样离开学校后，我们才能继续学习。一个真正会学习的人将是永远一帆风顺的；这是因为无论何时遇到他以前没有做过的事，他都会很快学会如何用最好的方法完成它。而没有受过教育的人要么无法完成，要么做得很糟。因此，学校的目的不应仅仅教授语言、算术、地理等科目，而且应该教会学生学习的方法。

To Learn How to Learn

Anonymous

Have you ever asked yourself why children go to school? You will probably say that they go to learn their own language and other languages, arithmetic, geography, geometry, history, science and all the other subjects. That is quite true; but why do they learn these things? And are these things all that they learn at school?

We send our children to school to prepare them for the time when they will be big and will have to work for themselves. They learn their own language so that they will be able to tell others clearly what they want and what they know, and understand what others tell them. They learn foreign languages in order to be able to benefit from what people in other countries have written and said, and in order to make people from other countries understand what they themselves mean. They learn arithmetic in order to be able to measure and count things in their daily life, geography in order to know something about the world around them, and history to know something about human beings they meet every day.Nearly everything they study at school has some practical use in their life, but is that the only reason why they go to school?

No. There is more in education than just learning facts. We go to school, above all, to learn how to learn, so that, when we have left school, we can continue to learn. A man who really knows how to learn will always be successful, because whenever he has to do something new which he has never had to do before, he will rapidly teach himself how to do it in the best way. The uneducated person, on the other hand, is either unable to do something new, or does it badly. The purpose of schools, therefore, is not just to teach languages,arithmetic, geography, etc., but teach pupils the way to learn.

三种目标

佚名

目标有三种:短期目标、中期目标和长期目标。

短期目标通常着眼于眼前的活动,人们可以以天为单位,逐日实施。这样的目标可以在一周或不到一周、或两周乃至数月内实现。人们不应忘记,没有坚固的基础就没有坚固的建筑物;同样,不去扎扎实实地实现短期目标,我们就不可能在实现长期目标上有大的作为。在完成长期目标之后,我们应当标明日期,并在已实现的目标基础上规划新的短期目标。

中期目标以短期目标为基础。中期目标可能涉及一个学期或整整一个学年,甚至可能延续数年之久。无论何时,每一次你只能向前迈一步,绝不能使自己失去信心或者把自己压得喘不过气来。这样每完成一步,你就会增强对自己能力的信心;你有发展潜力,可以事业有成。随着列出的目标实现日期表的加长,你的动力和要求也会增加。

长期目标可能与我们对未来的憧憬有关。长期目标可能跨越五年或者更长的时间。人生不是静止不变的。我们绝不应当让长期目标束缚我们的手脚,限制我们的行为。

Three Kinds of Goals

Anonymous

There are three kinds of goals: short−term, medium−term and long−term goals.

Short−term goals are those that usually deal with current activities,which we can apply on a daily basis. Such goals can be achieved in a week or less, or two weeks, or possibly months. It should be remembered that just as a building is no stronger than its foundation, our long−term goals cannot amount to very much without the achievement of solid short−term goals. Upon completing our short−term goals, we should date the occasion and then add new short−term goals that will build on those that have been completed.

The medium−term goals build on the foundation of the short−term goals. They might deal with just one term of school or the entire school year, or they could even extend for several years. Any time you move a step at a time, you should never allow yourself to become discouraged or overwhelmed. As you complete each step, you will enforce the belief in your ability to grow and succeed. And as your list of completion dates grow, your motivation and desire will increase.

Long−term goals may be related to our dreams of the future. They might cover five years or more. Life is not a static thing. We should never allow a long−term goal to limit us or our course of action.

与妈妈约会

佚名

结婚21年后，我发现了一种将爱的火花保持下去的新方法。我开始与另外一个女人出去约会。事实上，这还是我妻子替我出的主意呢。

"我知道你爱她。"有一天妻子对我说道，这使我大吃一惊。"但我也爱你。"我斩钉截铁地说。"我知道，不过，你也爱她。"

事实上，妻子想让我去拜访的另外一个女人是我的妈妈，她已经独自生活19年了，但是由于我的工作需要，加上3个孩子的牵绊，我很少有机会去看望她。一天晚上，我约她出来看电影。"出什么事了?你还好吗?"她问道。我的妈妈总是认为，深夜打电话或是事先没有任何征兆而突然登门造访，就意味着发生了什么不好的事情。"我觉得与您共度一段美好的时光将会是件令人愉快的事情，"我回答道，"就我们两个人。"她想了想，说道："我非常愿意。"

于是周五下班后，我便开车去接她。事实上我心里有些忐忑不安。当我到了妈妈的住所后才发现，她对这次约会也有些紧张。她穿好了外套站在门口等着我的到来。她还将头发盘了起来，并穿着最后一次庆祝结婚纪念日那天穿过的衣服。她的脸上带着微笑，就像一个天使一样容光焕发。"我对我的朋友们说，我要和儿子出去约会了，他们听了都很感动。"

上车时，她又接着说道："他们都迫切地想听我说说约会的情况呢!"

我们去了一家虽算不上是一流，但也十分优雅舒适的饭店。妈妈挽着我的手，样子看起来就像是第一夫人。我们坐下以后，便开始点菜。她只能看到一些大字。我偷偷看了一眼妈妈，却发现她也正盯着我，脸上还带着微笑，那微笑有种怀旧情结。"你小的时候，都是由我来看菜单的。"她说道。"现在您应该好好享受一下了，该是我回报您的时候了。"我回答道。

席间，我们谈得很愉快——也没什么特别的事——只是简单描述一下最近在彼此生活中所发生的事情。由于我们谈得太投入了，以至于连电影也错过了。晚些时候，我送她回家时，她对我说："我还会和你出去约会的，但下次必须我请你。"我同意了。"你们的晚宴进行得怎么样啊?"回家后妻子问我。"非常好，比我想象中的要好上许多倍。"我回答说。

仅仅几天以后，妈妈就由于心脏病突发永远离开了我们。事情发生得太过突然，以至于我还没有机会为她再做些什么事。就在那时，我明白了能够及时说出"我爱你"，并抽出时间陪陪自己所爱之人的重要。在你的生活中，没有什么比你的家庭更加重要。多花些时间陪陪你的家人吧，因为这些事情不能被推迟到"改天"。

Mamma

Anonymous

After 21 years of marriage, I discovered a new way of keeping alive the spark of love. I started to go out with another woman. It was really my wife's idea.

"I know that you love her," she said one day, taking me by surprise. "But I love you," I protested. "I know, but you also love her."

The other woman that my wife wanted me to visit was my mother, who has been a widow for 19 years, but the demands of my work and my three children had made it possible to visit her only occasionally. That night I called to invite her to go out for dinner and a movie. "What's wrong, are you well?" she asked. My mother is the type of woman who suspects that a late night call or a surprise invitation is a sign of bad news. "I thought that it would be pleasant to pass some time with you," I responded. "Just the two of us." She thought about it for a moment, then said, "I would like that very much."

That Friday after work, as I drove over to pick her up I was a bit nervous.When I arrived at her house, I noticed that she, too, seemed to be nervous about our date. She waited in the door with her coat on. She had curled her hair and was wearing the dress that she had worn to celebrate her last wedding anniversary She smiled from a face that was as

智慧英文励志篇

radiant as an angel's. "I told my friends that I was going to go out with my son, and they were impressed," she said, as she got into the car.

"They can't wait to hear about our meeting."

We went to a restaurant that, although not elegant, was very nice and cozy. My mother took my arm as if she were the First Lady. After we sat down, I had to read the menu. Her eyes could only read large print. Half way through the entries, I lifted my eyes and saw Mom sitting there stating at me. A nostalgic smile was on her lips. "It was I who used to have to read the menu when you were small, she said. " Then it's time that you relax and let me return the favor, " I responded.

During the dinner we had an agreeable conversation—nothing extraordinary—but catching up on recent events of each other's life. We talked so much that we missed the movie. As we arrived at her house later, she said, " I'll go out with you again,but only if you let me invite you. " I agreed." How was your dinner date? " asked my wife when I got home. " "very nice, Much more so than I could have imagined," I answered.

A few days later my mother died of a massive heart attack. It happened so suddenly that I didn't have a chance to do anything for her. At that moment I understood the importance of saying in time: "I love you" and to give our loved ones the time that they deserves. Nothing in life is more important than your family. Give them the time they deserve, because these things cannot be put off till "some other time" .

爷爷永远的伴侣

佚名

自孩提时代以来，我就看见爷爷左手腕上一直带着一块儿漂亮的手表，令我为之神往。那块儿表并没什么特别的，也不是什么昂贵的手表，但他有种特殊的魔力和特性，配上其主人正好。纳粹占领期间，爷爷就驻扎在法国。那时候需要一块儿手表，爷爷用他的维氏打火机（国际名牌，限量版本）跟一个当地酒馆里碰到的法国士兵换的。爷爷天真地把这块儿表当成他永恒的伴侣，从未离开过，即使是在战场上也没摘下来过。

我最早注意到这块儿手表是有次爷爷带我去附近湖里钓鱼。我们得拉着鱼线。坐在船上静静地待好几个小时，太阳懒洋洋地挂在天空，我们有一搭没一搭地说着些无关痛痒的话。爷爷偶尔会看着表坐立不安，要么收收鱼线，要么用手指摸摸手表金光闪闪的表面，有时他的脸上又全无表情。我那时是如此小，还不懂这么简单的一块儿手表有如此大的影响力。随着时间的流逝，我渐渐明白，他走哪儿都带着那块儿手表。有天我问他，这块儿手表有什么特别的。他告诉了我法国士兵的故事，他说这块儿表是个永恒的纪念，提醒着他是个幸运的人，可以在战后安全回家。而且，他说，它一向走得很准。

奶奶对此表却有不同的看法。过去的40年里，她每天都看见丈夫戴在手腕上的手表，她希望能换换，因此她给他买了一块儿新表。她问我，爷爷是否会喜欢，我回答说，他很可能会喜欢，可他绝不会戴它。奶奶从未真正地喜欢过那块儿老手表；她说

生命不息奋斗不止

Where There is Life, There is Struggle

因为它承载了太多关于战争的记忆，滑稽的是，它却代表了我生命中太多的美好时光。我想这仅仅是每个人观点不同而已。

爷爷对小礼物的反应正如我所预料的一样，他觉得这表挺好看的，可不明白奶奶为什么要给他买，这让奶奶知道他究竟有多喜欢他那块儿老式手表了。两个人都很固执，爷爷坚持不愿戴新表，奶奶又拒绝退掉新表，好像这么做就是认输了。

爷爷将盒子里的新表原封不动地收进了梳妆柜，这是表被闲置的最长时间。他不想伤害奶奶的感情而让她把新表退回去，但是他也不愿意戴它，最后这事儿就不了了之了。很多年以后，我问他为什么从未打开过，他的回答很简单，因为他已经有块手表了。他的回答如此简练，打消了我继续下去该话题的念头。

光阴似箭，岁月如梭，由于忙着各种各样的事情，处理各种各样的状况，我不能像往常一样经常去看望爷爷奶奶了。5年前，我接到奶奶的电话，通知我举行爷爷80大寿的生日宴会，我记得当时我着实大吃了一惊。尽管工作非常紧张，但我还是决定星期五请假，过个长周末去看望爷爷奶奶。星期五一大清早我就出发了，路上我一直想着那些数不尽的美好回忆，关于爷爷的事情和舒适的小农场。离上次看望他们都过去快两年了，我多希望能够好好休息一场。那个生日宴会跟大部分周六晚会一样，每个人都过得很愉快，尤其是爷爷。那天下午晚些时候，当所有客人都散去了，爷爷问我愿不愿意陪他去湖边走走，然后再放两条鱼线下湖钓钓鱼。他一定是在怀念我从小就和他一起钓鱼的时光，可我们好长时间没在一起过了。想到要与爷爷到湖边待一会儿，我觉得就这样结束一个难忘的日子再合适不过了。

湖面很平静，在阳光的照耀下闪闪发光，似乎在召唤我们投入它的宁静中去。我帮爷爷把旧船推到水里，令人吃惊的是，这么多年过去了，那条船居然还能用。爷爷带了一大罐蚯蚓。他总是说，这可是最好的鱼饵。我们把船划到湖心，穿上鱼饵抛下鱼线，然后等着鱼儿们上钩。这还是头一次我和爷爷有一整天的时间待在一起说说话，接下来的半个小时里，我们谈论着过去两年里所发生的事情。

显然鱼儿们都不饿，我正想说点儿什么，突然发现爷爷正目不转睛地盯着他的手表，并时不时地，慢慢地，满脸钟爱地用手指抚摸着它的水晶面，好像那是块有魔力的法宝似的，我问他是否有事。他慢慢地抬起头来凝视着我，眼睛里空洞无物。渐渐地，他的眼睛又恢复了独有的亮泽，满是皱纹的嘴边咧开了一丝神秘的笑意。我还没开口说话，他就把表从手腕上解下来了。然后抓住我的手放在手心里。他的这一举动

来得太突然，太出乎我意料了。我诧异无比地看着他，差点儿没接稳。本能地，我想把表还给他，但他合上了我的手，他那看我的眼神说明了一切。我有些不情愿地谢了他，然后他笑着说，他一直都知道我有多喜欢这块儿表，他觉得是时候把它传给我了。接下来钓鱼也没什么收获，只是有几次鱼轻轻地咬了鱼钩。

回到房里时，所有人都回家了，只有奶奶独自坐在厨房喝茶。我告诉她我累了想早点儿休息，也许会看会儿书。她谢谢我帮忙办了个如此成功的生日宴会。我无法告诉她船上发生的事情，于是我给了她一个拥抱，然后吻了她道过晚安就匆匆回房了。回到房间后，我从兜里掏出手表，翻过来放在手里，欣赏着它的分量——正如爷爷平常所说的，这是种质量的见证。过去长达半个世纪的岁月并未在上面留下多少痕迹。人们很容易会觉得它肯定没有50年。我把它戴到手腕上，很高兴它非常适合我，表链长短也不需要更换。我的脑子里有个问题在回响着，爷爷是怎么知道我总是想得到这块儿表的呢？

爷爷去世了，他死时还差一个星期就83岁了。遵从他的遗愿，我们把他埋在了湖边。每年他生日的那天，我都会到坟前来祭奠他。那条船还在那儿，有时我会划到湖心以纪念5年前那个特殊的日子，那天爷爷满足了我儿时的愿望，把表传给了我。从那天开始我就一直戴着它。

Grandpa's Constant Companion

Anonymous

Ever since I was a child, the watch that perpetually adorned my grandfather's left wrist had fascinated me. Not a particularly fancy or expensive watch, it seemed to have a certain charm and character about it that was strangely befitting of its owner. Grandpa was stationed in France during the Nazi occupation when, in need of a watch, he swapped his Zippo lighter for one owned by a French soldier he met in a local tavern. Grandpa would fondly refer to the watch as a constant companion that had never let him down, both on and off the battlefield.

The earliest I remember noticing the watch was when my grandfather would take me fishing at the nearby lake. We would spend hours in the boat with our lines in the water, taking about nothing in particular as the sun lazily crossed the sky. Occasionally Grandpa would fidget with the watch, whether to wind it or idly run his fingers over its shiny, gold surface. His face would sometimes lose all expression and, at such a young age, I couldn't understand how a simple wristwatch could garner such intense scrutiny. As the years went by, I became aware that he never went anywhere without the watch and I asked him one day what was so special about it. He told me the story of the French soldier and how the watch was a perpetual reminder that he was one of the fortunate ones to return home safely from the war. Besides, he said, it kept good time.

My grandmother had a different opinion of the watch. After seeing it on her husband's wrist every day for the past forty years, she opted for a slight change of scenery, so she bought him a new one. She asked me if I thought he would like it and I said he probably, would but that he would never wear it. Grandmom never did like that old watch; she said

65

there were too many bad war memorie associated with it. Ironically,the watch symbolized many of the more pleasurable times in my life. I suppose it' all a matter of perspective.

Grandpa reacted to his little present just like I had anticipated. He appreciated the watch but couldn't understand why she bought it when she knew how much he liked his old one. Both being equally stubborn, Grandpa insisted that he would never wear the new watch and Grandmom refused to return its as though by doing so would be an admission of defeat.

For the longest time the watch remained in its box on top of Grandpa's dresser. He didn't want to hurt Grandmom's feelings by returning it but he also couldn't bring himself to wear it, so eventually it was forgotten. Years later I asked him why he never wore it, he answered by simply saying he had one already. The terseness of his response discouraged me from pursuing the topic any further.

As time went by, events and situations in my life prevented me from seeing my grandparents as often as I once had. I remember five years ago getting a call from my grandmother regarding a surprise eightieth birthday party for Grandpa. My job had been exceptionally stressful so I decided to take that Friday off and spend a long weekend visiting with my grandparents. I left early Friday morning and throughout the entire trip I reminisced

about the countless memories that were born on my grandparents, cozy little farm. Nearly two years had slipped by since I had last been there and I was looking forward to some much–needed relaxation. The party went on for most of Saturday and everybody,especially Grandpa, had a wonderful time. Later that afternoon, when most of the guests had thinned out, Grandpa asked if I wanted to take a walk to the lake and throw a couple lines in the water. He must have been feeling quite nostalgic since we hadn't fished together since I was a kid. The thought of spending time with Grandpa out on the lake seemed like an appropriate way to end a memorable day.

The lake was placid with a golden sheen of sunlight sparkling on its surface,beckoning us to immerse ourselves in its tranquility. I helped Grandpa put the old boat in the water, surprised that it was still seaworthy after all of these years. Grandpa had brought a small container of nightcrawlers, the best bait for catching bass, he always said. We rowed out to the middle of the lake, baited our hooks and waited for the fish to do their part. This was the first time all day that I had a chance to talk. to him and we spent the next half–hour catching up on events of the past two years.

The fish apparently weren't very hungry and I was about to comment about it when I noticed Grandpa staring at his watch. Periodically he would run his finger slowly, almost lovingly, across the crystal face, as if it were a magical talisman. I asked him if he was okay and he slowly looked up at me, a dark, almost empty look in his eyes. Gradually, his eyes regained theiroriginal clarity and a cryptic smile formed on his wrinkled lips. Before I could say anything, he removed the watch from his wrist, grabbed my hand, and placed it in my open palm. The gesture was so sudden, so unexpected that I nearly dropped the watch as I stared at him in astonishment. Instinctively, I tried returning the watch but he closed my hand around it as he held my eyes with a look that spoke volumes of how he felt.Reluctantly, I thanked him and he smiled, saying that he always knew how much I liked the watch and he felt it was time to pass it on. The rest of the fishing trip passed by without incidence, except for a few nibbles on our fishing lines.

When we got back to the house everyone had gone home and my grandmother was alone in the kitchen drinking a cup of tea. I told her I was tired and wanted to turn in early and maybe read for a while. She thanked me for helping make the party such a success and I hugged and kissed her goodnight, unable to recount to her the events that took place on the boat. Once in my room I withdrew the watch from my pocket, turning it over in my hand and admiring its heft—a sign of quality, as Grandpa would often say. Time had been especially kind to the watch over the past half—century, and it easily could have passed for being no more than fifteen years old. I slipped it on my wrist and was pleased to find that it fit perfectly and the band wouldn't need adjusting. The question that kept echoing in my head was how Grandpa knew I had always wanted that watch.

My grandfather passed away a week shy off his eighty—third birthday and, in honor of his final wish, was buried by the lake. Each year, on his birthday, I make it a point to visit his grave and pay my respects. The boat is still.there and sometimes I'll row out to the middle of the lake to remember that special day five years ago when Grandpa fulfilled achildhood dream by passing on the watch;the same watch I've worn every day since.

持续了60年的爱情故事

佚名

那是几年前的一个寒冷的冬日,我在街上偶然拾到一个钱包。里面除了3美圆和一张看似好多年前的皱巴巴的信外,没有任何可以证明主人身份的东西。破旧的信封上,只有寄信人的地址还依稀可辨。我打开信,看到它写于1944年——60年前啊。我仔细读了一遍,希望能从中找出一些钱包主人的线索。这是一封绝交信,娟秀的字体告诉收信人迈克尔,她的母亲不准他们再见面。但不管怎样,她会永远爱他,署名是汉娜。

这是一封措辞优美的信,除了迈克尔这个名字外,信中没有其他可以识别失主的信息。或许咨询处的接线员能够按照信封上的地址查到电话号码。"您好,接线员!我有一个特殊的请求,我拾到一个钱包,正在努力寻找失主。钱包里只有一封信,您能否帮我按照信上的地址查到电话号码呢?"接线员把电话转到了主管处,主管说那个地址的电话虽然找得到,但是她不能告诉我号码。

但是,她说可以替我打电话问一下情况,若对方同意,她再和我联系。几分钟后她回了电话:"有位女士要和你讲话。"我问这位女士是否认识汉娜。"哦,当然认得!我们30年前买了汉娜家的房子。""那您知道他们现在住哪儿吗?"我问。"几年前汉娜不得已把她妈妈送去了养老院。那儿或许有人能提供一些汉娜的线索。"这位女士告诉了我这个养老院的名字。

我打电话给养老院,得知汉娜的母亲已经过世。接电话的女士又提供给我一个地址。她说汉娜也许会在那儿。我拨通了电话,接电话的女士说汉娜本人也住在养老院,并给了我号码。我打过去,主任告诉我说:"对,汉娜是在我们这儿。"我问是否可以去看她,这时已快晚上10点了。他说她可能睡了。"不过你可以来试试,没准儿她在休息室看电视呢!"主任和保安在养老院的门口等候我。

　　我们一起上三楼,见到了护理员。她说汉娜确实还在看电视。我们走进休息室。汉娜是一位和蔼可亲的白发老人,她面带微笑,友好地看着我。我把拾到钱包的事告诉了她,并把那封信拿给她看。

　　看到信时,她深深地吸了一口气。"年轻人,"她说,"这是我写给迈克尔的最后一封信。"她凝视了一会儿,忧郁地说"我非常爱他,但那时我只有16岁,妈妈认为我太小。他长的很帅,酷似演员肖恩·康奈利。"我们都笑了。

　　主任出去了,只剩下我们两个人在屋里。"他叫迈克尔·戈尔茨坦。如果你找到他,就请告诉他,我仍然非常挂念他,至今都没结婚。"她微笑着,泪水却夺眶而出。"我甚至想,根本没有人能配得上他……"与汉娜道过别,我乘电梯下了楼。

　　到门口时,保安问我:"那位老妇人能帮你什么忙吗?"我说她给了我些提示。"至少她告诉了我失主的名字。但是我不可能继续追查下去了。"我说我几乎整整一天都在寻找钱包的主人。

　　说着,我把那个镶着红花边的棕色皮钱包给保安看。他凑到跟前看了一眼说:"嗨,我好像在哪儿见过。是戈尔茨坦先生的,他常把它弄丢,我在大厅捡过三次。"我问:"谁是戈尔茨坦先生?""住在八楼的一位老人。一定是他的,他经常出去散步。"我谢过保安,又来到主任办公室,把保安的话告诉了他。他陪我来到了八楼。我希望戈尔茨坦还没睡。

　　"我想他一定还在休息室,"护理员说,"他晚上喜欢读书……他是一位很讨人喜欢的老人。"我们来到唯一那间亮着灯的房间,有位老人还在那儿看书呢。主任问他钱包是否丢了。迈克尔·戈尔茨坦翻了翻背包,然后说:"天啊! 真的不见了。""这位好心的先生捡到了一个,您看看是不是您的?"他看了一会儿欣慰地笑了。"是的,"他说,"就是它。一定是今天下午弄丢的。我该好好谢谢你。""哦,不必客气,"我说,"但我必须告诉你一件事,为了找到钱包主人,我读了里边的信。"他的笑容消失了:"你读了那封信?""我不仅读了信,而且还知道汉娜在哪儿。"

他的脸色顿时苍白。"汉娜?你知道她在哪儿?她生活得怎样?还是像年轻时那么漂亮吧?"我犹豫了一下没说什么。"求你快点告诉我!"迈克尔催促道。"她很好,并且和你认识她时一样漂亮。""你能告诉我她在哪儿吗?我明天想打电话给她。"

他抓着我的手说:"你一定知道一些事,是吗?当我收到那封信时,我的生活便终结了。我一直没结婚。我知道自己一直爱着她。"我说:"跟我来。"我们三人乘电梯来到了三楼。走进汉娜所在的那间休息室,她仍旧在那儿看电视。

主任走到她跟前轻声说:"汉娜,你认识这个人吗?"我和迈克尔站在门口等着她回答。她扶了一下眼镜,看了一会儿,但什么也没说。"汉娜,他是迈克尔,迈克尔·戈尔茨坦。你不认得了吗?""迈克尔?迈克尔?真的是你!"他慢慢地走到她跟前。她站起身来,他们幸福地拥抱,然后坐在沙发上,握紧彼此的手交谈起来。

我和主任走了出去,我们都感动得忍不住落泪了。我感叹道:"这就是命啊,命该如此!"三周后,我接到主任的电话,他问我:"你周日可以抽时间参加个婚礼吗?"他没等我答复,就迫不及待地说:"是迈克尔和汉娜,他们终于要步入婚姻的殿堂了!"

那是一场别开生面的婚礼,养老院的所有人都参加了。汉娜身穿米色礼服,看起来很漂亮。迈克尔身着深蓝色西装,显得分外高大。养老院为他们提供了一个单间。如果你想目睹76岁的新娘和78岁的新郎如年轻人一般相亲相爱的感人场面,那可一定要看看他们这幸福的一对儿。这个持续了60年的爱恋终于画上了一个完美的句号。

Letter In the Wallet

Anonymous

It was a freezing day, a few years ago, when I stumbled on a wallet in the street. There was no identification inside. Just three dollars, and a crumpled letter that looked as if it had been carded around for years. The only thing legible on the torn envelope was the return address. I opened the letter and saw that it had been written in 1944— almost 60 years ago. I read it carefully, hoping to find some clue to the identity of the wallet's owner. It was a "Dear John" letter. The writer, in a delicate script, told the recipient, whose name was Michael, that her mother forbade her to see him again. Nevertheless, she would always love him. It was signed Hannah.

It was a beautiful letter. But there was no way, beyond the name Michael, to identify

the owner. Perhaps if I called information the operator could find the phone number for the address shown on the envelope. "Operator, this is an unusual request. I'm trying to find the owner of a wallet I found. Is there any way you could tell me the phone number for an address that was on a letter in the wallet?" The operator gave me her supervisor, who said there was a phone listed at the address, but she could not give me the number.

However, she would call and explain the situation. Then, if the party wanted to talk, she would connect me. I waited a minute and she came back on the line. "I have a woman who will speak with you." I asked the woman if she knew a Hannah. "Oh, of course! We bought this house from Hannah's family thirty years ago." "Would you know where they could be located now?" I asked. "Hannah had to place her mother in a nursing home years ago. Maybe the home could help you track down the daughter." The woman gave me the name of the nursing home.

I called and found out that Hannah's mother had died. The woman I spoke with gave me an address where she thought Hannah could be reached. I phoned. The woman who answered explained that Hannah herself was now living in a nursing home. She gave me the number. I called and was told, "Yes, Hannah is with us." I asked if I could stop by to see her. It was almost 10 p.m..The director said Hannah might be asleep. "But if you want to take a chance, maybe she's in the day room watching television." The director and a guard greeted me at the door of the nursing home.

We went up to the third floor and saw the nurse, who told us that Hannah was indeed watching TV. We entered the day room. Hannah was a sweet, silver-haired old-timer with a warm smile and friendly eyes. I told her about finding the wallet and showed her the letter.

The second she saw it, she took a deep breath. "Young man," she said, "this letter was the last contact I had with Michael." She looked away for a moment, then said pensively, "I loved him very much. But I was only sixteen and my mother felt I was too young. He was so handsome. You know, like Sean Connery, the actor." We both laughed.

The director then left us alone. "Yes, Michael Goldstein was his name. If you find him, tell him I still think of him often. I never did marry," she said, smiling through tears that welled up in her eyes. "I guess no one ever matched up to Michael..." I thanked Hannah, said good—bye and took the elevator to the first floor.

As I stood at the door, the guard asked, "Was the old lady able to help you?" I told him she had given me a lead. "At least I have a last name. But I probably won't pursue it further for a while." I explained that I had spent almost the whole day trying to find the wallet's owner.

While we talked, I pulled out the brown—leather case with its red lanyard lacing and showed it to the guard. He looked at it closely and said, "Hey, I'd know that anywhere. That's Mr. Goldstein's. He's always losing it. I found it in the hall at least three times." "Who's Mr. Goldstein?" I asked. "He's one of the old—timers on the eighth floor. That's Mike Goldstein's wallet, for sure. He goes out for a walk quite often." I thanked the guard and ran back to the director's office to tell him what the guard had said. He accompanied me to the eighth floor. I prayed that Mr. Goldstein would be up.

"I think he's still in the day room," the nurse said. "He likes to read at night...a darling old man." We went to the only room that had lights on, and there was a man reading a book. The director asked him if he had lost his wallet. Michael Goldstein looked up, felt his back pocket and then said, "Goodness, it is missing." "This kind gentleman found a wallet. Could it be yours?" The second he saw it, he smiled with relief. "Yes," he said, "that's it. Must have dropped it this afternoon. I want to give you a reward." "Oh, no thank you," I said. "But I have to tell you something. I read the letter in the hope of finding out who owned the wallet." The smile on his face disappeared. "You read that letter?" "Not only did I read it, I think I know where Hannah is."

He grew pale. "Hannah? You know where she is? How is she? Is she still as pretty as she was?" I hesitated. "Please tell me! " Michael urged. "She's fine, and just as pretty as when you knew her." "Could you tell me where she is? I want to call her tomorrow."

He grabbed my hand and said, "You know something? When that letter came, my life ended. I never married. I guess I've always loved her." "Michael," I said. "Come with me." The three of us took the elevator to the third floor. We walked toward the day room where Hannah was sitting, still watching TV.

The director went over to her. "Hannah," he said softly, "do you know this man?" Michael and I stood waiting in the doorway. She adjusted her glasses, looked for a moment, but didn't say a word. "Hannah, it's Michael. Michael Goldstein. Do you remember?" "Michael? Michael? It's you! " He walked slowly to her side. She stood and they embraced. Then the two of them sat on a couch, held hands and started to talk.

The director and I walked out, both of us crying. "See how the good Lord works," I said philosophically. "If it's meant to be, it will be." Three weeks later, I got a call from the director who asked, "Can you break away on Sunday to attend a wedding?" He didn't wait for an answer. "Yup, Michael and Hannah are going to tie the knot! "

It was a lovely wedding, with all the people at the nursing home joining in the celebration. Hannah wore a beige dress and looked beautiful. Michael wore a dark blue suit and stood tall. The home gave them their own room, and if you ever wanted to see a 76 – year –old bride and a 78 –year –old groom acting like two tunagens, you had to see this couple. A perfect ending for a love affair that had lasted nearly 60 years.

聆听心灵

佚名

就在你刚被带到这个世界瞬间,你就开始了对自己心灵的聆听。当你来到这个世界的前两年还不能开口说话时,你就在用心灵去诠释和领会世间万物。

心灵的声音是人内心下意识的反应。内心的下意识总是扮演着个体思想观点的第二级反应的角色。它用理性评断和诠释着人世间的是非对错。当我们行事逆反了内心的旨意时,我们就会有愧疚感,并将为此烦恼终生。

时常,在我们感情压抑或那些让我们失望的瞬间总是难以忘怀时,我们似乎需要某种情绪和精神上的支撑。通常,当多数悲伤发生时,我们会向最亲密的伙伴或者最亲爱的家人倾诉心声,以减轻我们的压力。因为有了那些感同身受的倾听者,我们就能扫去精神焦虑和情绪紧张而带来的最初的阴霾。我们突然感觉到的精神焕发是因为我们心灵之声警惕我们对万事万物泰然处之,并且将一切过往都遗留在我们大脑的记忆深处!

绝大多数时候,我们的心灵的声音还是正确的,因为它比任何人,甚至比我们自身更了解我们。它是直觉这个胆大恶魔的孩子,从小,它就一直和我们相伴。很多时候凭直觉办事还是有益的,因为它是我们智能和体能同步提供的反应。

无论何时你尝试着抽第一根香烟,或者你不得不站在一场争论的其中一方时。你总会有进退两难的感觉。此时,心灵会自主地作出裁定,毫不夸张地说,它会为我们将来带来不快乐的因素。当这些问题迎面而来时,我们或者忽视内心的士气鼓舞者,或者走进这个世界,去探寻精神寄托和快乐起源。

Listen to Your Inner Voice

Anonymous

Very much, ever since you were brought into this world. When you couldn't open your mouth till the first two years on planet earth, inner voice is the one through which you interpreted and understood things.

Inner voice is the voice of mouth of the subconscious mind. The subconscious mind is always acting as a secondary reflector of thoughts and ideas in the body. It justifies and rationalizes what is right and what is wrong. When we go against what the inner voice says we get a guilty conscious and are bothered by it throughout our lives.

At times when we are feeling low or those unforgettable moments when we are let down, we seem to need some kind of emotional or mental support. We usually speak to our closest pal or our dearest family member during times of distress to ease the burden. At such times we get over the initial drizzle of emotional anxiety and mental restlessness, because of the pepping up by our empathic listener. We suddenly feel rejuvenated because our inner voice alerts us to get on with things and leave the things of past on the memory books of our brain.

The inner voice is always right most of the times because it knows us better than others and probably even ourselves. It is the dare devil child of the intuitions which we have been having since childhood. It's good to go by intuitions most of the times because it's the response provided due to the synchronism between our mental and physical being.

Whenever you are trying your first cigarette, or whenever you are asked to take sides in an argument, you are always in a sense of dilemma. During these times your inner voice automatically gives its verdict, which when over written, might leave us unhappy in the future. It's up to us to either ignore the morale booster inside us or go out to the world and search for spiritual guru's and happiness, when all these things are very much present within us.

生活的乐趣

佚名

生活的乐趣源自美好的情感,相信这些情感,让它们如鸟儿般自由地在天空翱翔。生活中的快乐永远不能伪装得来。拥有快乐生活的人无须言语,就会用快乐感染他人。他们将快乐释放,让快乐发光,用快乐的光芒照耀他人的生活,就像鸟儿奉献自己的歌声一样。

仅仅为追求生活的乐趣而努力,永远不会成功。它如同幸福一样,只会跟随有更高追求的人。它是伟大而简单的生活的附属品,生活的乐趣源自我们对其的投入,而非索取。

The Joy of Living

Anonymous

The joy in living comes from having fine emotions, trusting them, giving them the freedom of a bird in the open. Joy in living can never be assumed as a pose, or put on from the outside as a mask. People who have this joy don't need to talk about it;they radiate it. They just live out their joy and let it splash its sunlight and glow into other lives as naturally as bird sings.

We can never get it by working for it directly. It comes, like happiness, to those who are aiming at something higher. It is a byproduct of great, simple living. The joy of living comes from what we put into living, not from what we seek to get from it.

排遣压力, 享受生活

佚名

假期又来临了。大部分人都很期待它的到来。但是由于我们将自己沉浸在整个假期中——聚会、购物、烹饪、串亲戚,清帐——我们所期盼的,聚在一起的快乐和温暖的感觉,常常会带来少许的压力和疲倦。

在激情时刻做到没有压迫感几乎是不可能的, 这里有一些方法可以使这些压迫感保持平衡。考虑以下几个小点,会给你的假期增添些许快乐。

——在假期时还要坚持锻炼,即使强度比平常稍稍减轻一点。

——努力多吃健康食品。

在聚会和其他假期活动的间隙要多休息。

——留心来自心底的声音。

你是否错过了一个儿时的特别假期仪式?你能否把它安排在你现在的假期日程中?

——学会宽容。

记住每一个排着长队购物的人都会像你一样担心时间。(不过最好可以选择网上购物!)

——懂得取舍。

你不能做所有想做的事,如果你尝试一下,其实并不开心。

——提前预算假期的开支。

列一个花销清单,并遵循它。

——记住饮酒只会使你有感觉舒服和压力减轻的幻觉。

饮酒时需要注意的就是适度——特别是当许多压力同时出现时的假期。

——在家庭聚会中避开艰难或敏感的话题。

——施与他人少许救济。

救济一个贫穷家庭。给穷困的孩子一些玩具。记住施与是假期的真正快乐。

如果你的家庭有些变化,或是因为一些原因你不能与你爱的人共度假期,去寻找与你处于同样境地的人们共度一个特别的假期。

——向朋友倾诉,或者,如果需要的话,找一位临床医学家,把你假期里的郁闷与压力告诉他。

通常,将自己的心事吐露出来,有助于缓解消极的情绪,而且交流可以给你提供一个缓解压力的环境。

——感激你所拥有的一切。

Ways to Minimize Stress

Anonymous

It's holiday again. Most of us look forward to it. But as we immerse ourselves in the holiday season—the parties, the shopping, the cooking, the relatives, the bills—what we were hoping for, fun and warm feelings of togetherness,often turns out to be little more than stress and fatigue.

Although it is nearly impossible not to experience some increase in stress during this hectic time, there are ways to help keep stress levels manageable. Consider the following tips to help make your holidays a little brighter.

—Continue to exercise during the holidays, even if it's less than your usual regimen.

—Try to eat healthy foods.

Relax between parties and other holiday obligations.

—Be aware of what's going on inside of you.

Are you missing a special holiday ritual from your childhood? Can you incorporate it in to your current holiday plans?

—Practise tolerance.

Remember that everyone in those long shopping lines is just as pressed for time as you are. (Better yet shop online!)

—Prioritize, prioritize, prioritize.

You cannot do it all, and if you try, you surely will not enjoy yourself.

—Budget your holiday spending money ahead of time.

Write down your spending list and stick to it.

—Remember that drinking alcohol only gives the illusion of feeling better and less stressed.

It is important to drink only in moderation—particularly during the holidays when many other stresses are present.

—Avoid bringing up dificult or sensitive subject matter at family gatherings.

—Give to someone less fortunate.

Adopt a needy family. Donate toys for underprivileged children. Remember that giving is the true spirit of the holidays.

—If you are from a displaced family, or for some reason cannot be with your loved ones during the holidays, seek out others in the same situation and plan a special gathering.

—Talk to a friend, or, if needed, a therapists, about your holiday blues and stress.

Often,just verbalizing your thoughts will help alleviate the negative feelings, and the interchange can provide you with some stress—relief solutions.

—Be thankful for all you have.

生活是一所全日制学校

佚名

你是"生活"这所全日制学校的学生，每天都有机会学习各种课程。无论你喜欢与否，这些都是你的必修课。

为什么你会生活在这里？你生活的目的何在？长久以来，人们都在探寻人生的意义，然而，每一代人都忽略了一个事实——人生的意义并没有答案，它是因人而异的。

人各有志，每个人的人生目的和道路都不尽相同。在人生的旅途上，你需要不断地学习，只有这样，才有望实现人生目标。你所学的知识是特意为你而设的，而探寻人生意义、实现人生目标的关键则在于认真学习这些经验并吸取教训。

在生命旅程中，别人不必面对的挑战和教训，你或许要面对；当然，别人为之奋斗多年的诸多挑战，你也许不必应对。你拥有幸福的婚姻，而你的朋友却要饱尝婚姻之苦、承受离婚之痛，这些你大概永远都不会弄明白。同样，对于你疲于奔命，却过着拮据的生活，而你的同辈却过着安逸优越的生活，你也可能无法理解。但有一点是肯定的，就是那些注定要学的知识与经验你定会有缘见识。至于是否愿意学，则完全取决于你自己。

因此，这里的挑战在于你要汲取各种不同的经验和教训，以使你的生活符合自己独特的人生道路。这是你一生都要面对的最严峻的挑战。之所以这样说，是因为人生道路各有差别。但是，谨记——不要与周围的人相比，不要计较不同的经验和教训。你要学的东西是你力所能及的，并且是特意为你的成长制定的。

事事公正、人人平等是我们的愿望，这就是所谓的公平感。然而，事实上，生活并非总是公平的，或许命运不应该这样安排，但你的人生就是有可能比别人艰辛、坎坷。每个人的情况不同，所以，也该用不同的方法对待自己的境遇。若想拥有平和的心境，就不可存有悲观厌世的心态。过于计较世事的不公，容易自轻自贱，从而发现不了自己的独特之处。因受愤世嫉俗、懊恼烦闷的情绪干扰，你也许会错过许多自己该学的课程。

A Full-time School Called Life

Anonymous

You are enrolled in a full-time school called "life". Each day in this school you will have the opportunity to learn lessons. You may like the lessons or hate them, but you have to design them as part of your curriculum.

Why are you here? What is your purpose? Humans have sought to discover the meaning of life for long time. What we and our ancestors have overlooked, however, is that there is no answer. The meaning of life is different for every individual.

Each person has his or her own purpose and distinct path, unique and separating from others. As you walk on your life path, you will be presented with numerous lessons that you will need to learn in order to fulfill that purpose. The lessons you are presented with are specific to you. Learning these lessons is the key to discovering and fulfilling the meaning and relevance of your own life.

As you travel through your lifetime, you may encounter challenging lessons that others

智慧英文励志篇

don't have to face, while others spend years struggling with challenges that you don't need to deal with. You may never know why you are blessed with a wonderful marriage, while your friends suffer through bitter arguments and painful divorces, just as you cannot be sure why you struggle financially while your peers enjoy abundance. The only thing you can count on for certain is that you will be presented with all the lessons that you Specifically need to learn; whether you choose to learn them or not is entirely up to you.

The challenge here, therefore, is to align yourself with your own unique path by learning individual lessons. This is one of the most difficult challenges you will face in your lifetime, as sometimes your path will be radically different from others.But, remember, don't compare your path to the people around you and don't focus on the disparity between their lessons and yours. You need to remember that you will only be faced with lessons that you are capable of learning, and the lessons are specific to your own growth.

Our sense of fairness is the expectation of equity—the assumption that all things are equal and that justice will always prevail. In fact, life is not fair, and you may indeed have a more difficult life path than others around you,deserved or not.Everyone's circumstances are unique, and everyone needs to handle his or her own circumstances differently. If you want to move toward serenity, you will be required to move out of the complaining phase of "it's not fair" . Focusing on the unfairness of circumstances keeps you comparing yourself with others rather than appreciating your own special uniqueness. You miss out on learning your individual lessons by distracting yourself with feelings of bitterness and resentment.

如何安度晚年

伯特兰·罗素

　　从心理学方面来说，在老年时期有这样两种危险需要我们加以防范。其一是过度沉迷于过去。生活在回忆中，对过去的美好时光感到遗憾，或为死去的朋友悲伤痛苦，这些都是没有用处的。人的思想应该直面未来，做一些尚力所能及的事情。要做到这样并不是容易的事，因为一个人的过去时刻都在逐渐增加分量。人们很容易想到自己过去的情感比现在更加生动丰富，过去的思想比现在更加深刻。如果这是真的那它就应该被忘掉，如果它被遗忘那它大概就不会是真的。

　　另一件事是避免依附于年轻人，希望从他们的活力中汲取动力。当你的孩子们已长大成人，他们想要过属于自己的生活，如果你仍然像他们小时候那样对他们倍加关心，你很可能会成为他们的负担，除非他们对此异常淡漠。我并不是说我们应该毫不关心他们，但是你的关心应该是理性的、如果可能还应是仁慈的，但并非是感情用事。动物在自己的后代一旦可以生活自理时，便不再照看它们，然而，对人类来说，因幼年期很长，做到这点是很难的。

　　我觉得对于那些有很多兴趣爱好，包括一些适宜的活动的人来说，享有一个成功的晚年是很容易的。正是在这个领域之中，长期积累的经验会结出累累的硕果，通过经验获得的智慧可以不受任何压制释放出来。告诫成年的孩子不让他们犯错误是没有用的，不仅因为他们不信任你,而且因为错误也是教育不可缺少的一部分。但如果你的兴趣爱好比较贫乏,除非你寄希望于儿孙后辈,否则你会感到生活空虚无聊。在那种情况下,你必须要意识到尽管你仍然可以给他们提供物质上的方便,比如给他们补贴或给他们织几件毛衣等。但你千万不要期望他们会喜欢与你为伴。

　　一些老人受困于对死亡的恐惧。年轻人有这样的恐惧是合情理的。年轻人有理由害怕死在战场,他们想到被骗去了的生活可以给予的美好事物时,同样有理由感到痛苦。但若有一个老人历经人世间喜怒哀乐,并完成了应做的一切后,仍然害怕死亡,那就不是件什么体面的事了。

　　战胜这种恐惧最有效的方法就是——至少我是这样认为的——就是使你兴趣爱好的范围逐渐变宽广,不患得患失,直到生活丰富多彩起来。一个人的一生就像是一条河——开始是涓涓细流,在两岸紧紧的束缚之下,热情奔放地冲过岩石和瀑布。河水逐渐变得宽起来,两岸渐渐退缩。河水流得更加平静,直到最后无声无息地与大海融为一体,毫无痛苦地失去自身的存在。可以用这样的方式看待生命的老年人,是不会感到对死亡的恐惧的,因为他所关心的事会继续存在。如果随着精力的衰退,疲惫之感日益增加。休息的念头也不再是件不受欢迎的事。我希望能在工作时死去,因为知道有人会把我再也不能做的这项工作继续下去,同时为自己已经完成的力所能及的一切感到满意。

How to Grow Old

(British)Bertrand Russell

Psychologically there are two dangers to be guarded against in old age.One of these is undue absorption in the past. It does not do to live in memories, in regrets for the good old days, or in sadness about friends who are dead.One's thoughts must be directed to the future, and to things about which there is something to be done. This is not always easy; one's own past is a gradually increasing weight. It is easy to think to oneself that one's emotions used to be more vivid than they are, and one's mind more keen. If this is true it should be forgotten, and if it is forgotten it will probably not be true.

The other thing to be avoided is clinging to youth in the hope of sucking vigour from its vitality. When your children are grown up they want to live their own lives and if you continue to be as interested in them as you were when they were young, you are likely to become a burden to them, unless they are unusually callous. I do not mean that one should be without interest in them, but one's interest should be contemplative and, if possible, philanthropic, but notunduly emotional. Animals become indifferent to their young as soon as their young can look after themselves, but human beings, owing to the length of infancy, find this difficult.

I think that a successful old age is easiest for those who have strong impersonal interests involving appropriate activities. It is in this sphere that long experience is really fruitful, and it is in this sphere that the wisdom born of experience can be exercised without being oppressive. It is no use telling grown-up children not to make mistakes, both because they will not believe you, and because mistakes are an essential part of education; but if you are one of those who are incapable of impersonal interests, you may find that your life will be empty unless you concern yourself with your children and grandchildren. In that case you must realize that while you can still render them material services,such as making them an allowance or knitting them jumpers, you must not expect that they will enjoy your company.

Some old people are oppressed by the fear of death. In the young there is a justification for this feeling. Young men who have reason to fear that they will be killed in battle may justifiably feel bitter in the thought that they have been cheated of the best things that life has to offer. But in an old man who has known human joys and sorrows, and has achieved whatever work it wad in him to do, the fear of death is somewhat abject and ignoble.

The best way to overcome it so at least it seems to me is to make your interests gradually wider and more impersonal, until bit by bit the universal life.An individual human existence should be like a fiver small at first, narrowly contained within its banks, and rushing passionately past rocks and over waterfalls. Gradually the fiver grows wider, the banks recede, the waters flow more quietly, and in the end, without any visible break, they become merged in the sea, and painlessly lose their individual being. The man who, in old age, can see his life in this way, will not suffer from the fear of death, since the things he cares for will continue. And if, with the decay of vitality, weariness increases,the thought of rest will not be unwelcome. I should wish to die while still at work, knowing that others will carry on what I can no longer do and content inthe thought that what was possible has been done.

生命就是希望

　　我在俄亥俄州读八年级时,班上有一个叫海伦的女孩,她遭遇了一场严重的车祸。她因害怕错过公交车而匆忙跑去,结果不慎在冰上滑倒,跌倒在了公交车的后轮之下。尽管她在事故中幸存了下来,她腰部以下却瘫痪了。我去看望了她,那时,13岁的我想,从此以后,她再也不能过正常人的生活了。

　　多年以后,我搬了家,从此就再没想到过海伦。三年前,在佛罗里达州,我大儿子骑车时被一辆汽车撞倒,造成脑部严重创伤。当我正在照看儿子时,一位自称是医院义务工作人员的女士打来了电话。那正是最受煎熬的时刻。我毫无缘由地失声痛哭并挂了电话。

　　不一会儿,一位坐着轮椅的漂亮女士,手中拿着一盒纸巾,转动着轮椅来到我儿子的病房。十六年过去了。我仍然认出是海伦。她微笑着,把纸巾递给我并拥抱我。我告诉了她我是谁,我们都为此感到震惊,之后,她开始给我讲述分别后她的生活经历。她结了婚并且有了孩子,她还获得了学位,这样她可以给那些比她更不幸的人带去希望。她告诉我如果她有什么东西可以给我,那就是"希望"了。

　　看着这位了不起并乐于奉献的女士,我感到了自己的渺小。但是,这是自从儿子受伤后,我第一次感受到希望。从这位我曾以为丧失了生活资格的人身上,我学到了:只要还有生命,就有希望。我的儿子奇迹般地康复了,我们又搬回了北方。然而,我将永远无法偿还我欠下海伦的这份情。

Where There is Life, There is Hope

Anonymous

When I was in the 8th grade in Ohio, a girl named Helen in my class who had a terrible accident. As she was running to the bus in order not to miss it, she slipped on some ice and fell under the rear wheels of the bus. She survived the accident, but was paralyzed from the waist down. I went to see her, in my 13–year–old mind thinking she wouldn't live normally from then on.

Over the years, I moved and didn't think much about Helen after that. Three years ago, in Florida, my oldest son was hit by a car while riding his bike, causing a terrible brain injury. While I was looking after my son, a lady who said she was the hospital's social worker called. It was a particularly trying day. I burst into tears for no reason and hung up.

A short time later, a beautiful woman, in a wheelchair, rolled into my son's room with a box of tissues. After 16 years, I still recognized Helen. She smiled, handed me the tissues and hugged me. I told her who I was, and after we both got through the shock of that, she began to tell me about her life since we last saw each other. She had married, had children and gotten her degree so that she could smooth the path for those less fortunate than her. She told me that if there was anything she could give me, is would be hope.

Looking at this wonderful, giving person, I felt small. But I also felt the first hope I had felt since learning that my son was hurt. From this person that I thought would have no quality of life, I learned that where there is life, there is hope. My son miraculously recovered and we moved back north, but I owe Helen a debt that I can never repay.

幸与不幸

佚名

幸福就是一种态度。你可以选择苦难，也可以选择幸福和坚强。

渐渐地，我开始相信，生活中的幸和不幸是人脑的产物，是对现实的一种理解，是对现实生活的所思所想。我在这儿谈的不是悲观论或是乐观论的问题，而是另一个问题，即怎样阐释自己的生活以及自己对生活的态度。

人们往往被自己的需求和目标牵着走，忘记了他们已经取得的和已经实现的成就，舍不得花时间享受胜利成果或者为自己已经获得的成功而高兴。永无止境的需求和渴望，冲淡了成功的喜悦，并使我们感觉自己离原定目标越来越远。

如果我们能偶尔停下来，花点时间环顾四周，品味一下我们所获得的成功，感受一下生活中的点点滴滴，欣赏一下身边最平凡最简单的美，回顾一下我们走过的每一步，哪怕它微乎其微，都会让我们对自己、对生活充满信心。这样，我们就会觉得，别的目标都是可行的、是有能力达到的；我们就会觉得，今后的生活充满了希望。

心怀梦想，着眼未来是件好事，但我们不能一味地沉浸在未来之中而忽略了现在，忽略了我们所应享受的幸福。不管怎样，在着眼于美好未来的同时，我们更要脚踏实地享受现在的成功，现在才是重要的！

Happiness and Misery

Anonymous

Happiness is an attitude. We either make ourselves miserable, or happy and strong.

I've come to believe that Happiness and Misery in life are a product of the human brain and it's conception of reality. It's all in the way you look at the things around you and how you think of them. This is not the half−empty−or−half−full−glass idea I'm talking about, it's about how you interpret your life and your position in it.

People tend to get carried away by their needs and by their goals,forgetting about the things they've already reached and realized, not taking the time to enjoy them or be happy about their successes. The everlasting need and thirst for more downsizes our successes and makes us feel like we're still far away from where we want to be.

But if we just took the time and stopped every once in a while,looked around us and savoured the taste of the successes we've reached, the little things in life that we have, the beauty of the smallest and simplest things surrounding us, and even the tiny steps that we've taken we'd truly feel a lot better about ourselves and our lives. And then we'd look at our other goals as ones that are reachable and doable, and as a life that extends ahead of us full of promise.

It's great to have a great ambition and to always look into the future, but we shouldn't get too obsessed with the future and too engulfed in our goals that we forget to live our present and enjoy it.Keep your eyes on the future, but keep your feet on the ground and enjoy the present for what it's worth.

幸福絮语

佚名

最幸福的人未必拥有全部最好的东西，他们只是能够最大程度地利用生活所赋予的一切。

也许，上帝希望我们在遇到适合自己的人之前，总会遇到一些不适合自己的人，这样，在最终找到适合自己的人的时候，我们就会心存感激，并将其看作天赐福祉。

当一扇幸福之门关闭的时候，另一扇幸福之门就会打开，但是，我们往往长久地凝望着那扇已经关上的门，而没有看见那扇已经打开的门。

如果有一个人与你一同心情愉悦地坐在门廊里，然后没说一句话就走了，但当他离开后，你却感觉你们之间仿佛有过你平生最美妙的交谈，那么这个人就是你最好的朋友。

凡事都是失去之后，才知珍惜；同样，不曾拥有，也就不知有所缺憾。

爱别人并不意味着一定会得到对方的爱！不要期待爱的报答，要等待爱在对方心中滋长，如果没能如愿的话，那就让爱常驻你心吧！对一个人产生好感只需要一分钟，喜欢上一个人需要一个小时，爱上一个人需要一天，而忘记一个人却需要漫长的一生。

不要追求容貌，那是骗人的。别去追逐财富，那最终会烟消云散的。去寻找那些能使你绽放笑容的人吧！因为只有欢笑才能给黑暗的日子带来光明。找一个能博你开心一笑的人吧！

在我们的生命中，有时，你是如此地思念一些人以至于你希望他们能从梦境中跳出来，让你能够实实在在地去拥抱。

梦你想梦之梦，去你想去之地，做你想做之人吧！因为你只有一次生命和一次机会去做自己想做的事情。

愿你，因拥有幸福而可爱，因经历考验而坚强，因体验悲伤而善良，因怀抱希望而幸福。

设身处地为别人着想。如果你觉得受到了伤害，对方恐怕也是如此。

最幸福的人未必拥有全部最好的东西，他们只是能够最大程度地利用生活所赋予的一切。

幸福青睐那些哭过、伤过、追寻过并且努力过的人们，因为只有他们才懂得珍惜曾经影响过自己生命的人。爱以笑开始，因吻而深厚，却以泪结束。最光明的未来往往建立在忘记过去的基础上，只有当你让过去的失败与伤痛随风而逝时，才能更好地生活下去。

当你出生的时候，你不停地哭泣，周围的人都在微笑。好好地度过你的一生。这样，当你死去时，你可以面带微笑，尽管周围的人在为你哭泣。

请将本文传递给那些对你来说很重要的人，那些以这样或那样的方式影响你生活的人，那些在你需要时带给你欢笑的人，那些在你失落时让你看到光明的人，那些你渴望结交并成为挚友的人。如果你还没有这样做，也不用担心，在你的身上不会发生任何糟糕的事情，你只是错过了用这篇美文让别人的日子变得更美好的机会。

Happiness Message

Anonymous

The happiest people don't necessarily have the best of everything; they just make the most of everything that comes along their way.

Maybe God wants us to meet a few wrong people before meeting the right one so that when we finally meet the right person, we will know how to be grateful for that gift.

When the door of happiness closes, another opens, but we often look so long at the closed door that we don't see the one which has been opened for us.

The best kind of friend is the kind you can sit on a porch and swing with, never say a word, and then walk away feeling like it was the best conversation you've ever had.

It's true that we don't know what we've got until we lose it, but it's also true that we don't know what we've been missing until it arrives.

Giving someone all your love is never an assurance that they'll love you back! Don't expect love in return; just wait for it to grow in their heart but if it doesn't, be content it grew in yours. It takes only a minute to get a crush on someone, an hour to like someone, and a day to love someone, but it takes a lifetime to forget someone.

Don't go for looks; they can deceive; Don't go for wealth, even that fades away. Go for someone who makes you smile because it only takes a smile to make a dark day seem bright. Find the one that makes your heart smile.

There are moments in life when you miss someone so much that you just want to pick them from your dreams and hug them for real!

Dream what you want to dream; go where you want to go; be what you want to be, because you have only one life and one chance to do all the things you want to do.

May you have enough happiness to make you sweet, enough trials to make you strong, enough sorrow to keep you humane, enough hope to make you happy.

Always put yourself in others'shoes. If you feel that it hurts you, it probably hurts the other person, too.

The happiest people don't necessarily have the best of everything; they just make the most of everything that comes along their way.

Happiness lies for those who cry, those who hurt, those who have searched, and those who have tried, for only they can appreciate the importance of people who have touched their lives. Love begins with a smile, grows with a kiss and ends with a tear. The brightest future will always be based on a forgotten past, you can't go on well in life until you let go of your past failures and heartaches.

When you were born, you were crying and everyone around you was smiling. Live your life so that when you die, you're the one who is smiling and everyone around you is crying.

Please send this message to those people who mean something to you, to those who have touched your life in one way or another, to those who make you smile when you really need it, to those that make you see the brighter side of things when you are really down, to those who you want to let them know that you appreciate their friendship. And if you don't, don't worry, nothing bad will happen to you, you will just miss out on the opportunity to brighten someone's day with this message.

梦想

佚名

将目光锁定在你所拥有的东西上，而不是你想要的东西上，这样，你才会知道什么是心满意足。

从前，有一个男孩住在山上的一所大房子里。他喜欢狗、喜欢马、喜欢跑车、喜欢音乐。他爬树，游泳，打橄榄球，当然，还追求漂亮的女孩子。要是没有做家务的琐事，他的生活极为完美。

有一天，男孩对上帝说："我一直在想，当我成为一个男人后想要得到什么东西，现在我知道了。"

"什么东西呢？"上帝问道。

"我想住在一幢大房子里，房前有门廊，门廊旁还有两条圣伯纳德狗，屋后有花园。我想要娶一位长着蓝眼睛、有着乌黑长发、身材高挑、温柔动人的女人为妻。她不但会弹吉他，而且唱起歌来，声音悠扬动听。"

"我希望能有三个健壮的儿子，我们可以一起打橄榄球。长大后，我希望他们中的一个能够成为伟大的科学家，另一个能够当上参议员，最小的儿子能在49人橄榄球队当四分卫。"

"另外，我希望成为一名探险家，可以在浩瀚无边的大海上航行，可以攀登绝壁，可以抢险救援。我希望能开上一辆红色的法拉利跑车。当然，今后我再也不想自己做家务了。"

"哦，这听起来可真是一个不错的梦想。"上帝说，"我想要你幸福。"

一天，男孩打橄榄球时，膝盖受伤。伤好之后。他再也不能登山了，甚至连大树也爬不上去，更不用说在浩瀚无边的海洋中航行了。于是，他学做营销，并开了一家医疗用品公司。后来，他娶了一位漂亮温柔的女子为妻，她有着一头乌黑的长发。不过，她的个子不高,眼睛是褐色的而不是蓝色的。她既不会弹吉他,也不会唱歌,不过,她能用珍稀的中国调料烧一手好菜,而且她画的鸟儿栩栩如生。

由于生意的关系,他住在城市中一栋高层公寓楼的最高层。从这里,可以俯瞰蔚蓝的大海和城市中的万家灯火。他没有地方养圣伯纳德狗,但他养了一只毛茸茸的小猫。他有三个非常漂亮的女儿,其中坐在轮椅里的小女儿最可爱。三个女儿都非常爱他,虽然她们不能陪他打橄榄球,但是有时他们一起到公园里掷飞碟,他的小女儿虽然不能上场,但她会坐在树荫下,弹着吉他,唱起美妙悠扬的歌曲。他赚了很多钱,生活无忧无虑,但是他却没有开红色的法拉利跑车。有时,他还不得不收拾东西,即使有些东西不是他的,毕竟,他有三个女儿。

一天早晨,就在他醒来的那一刻,他突然想起了小时候曾经做过的那个梦。

"我真的好难过,"他跟最好的朋友说。

"怎么了?"朋友问道。

"因为我曾经梦想着娶一位身材高挑、长着黑头发、蓝眼睛而且会弹吉他、会唱歌的女人为妻。但是,我现在的妻子既不会弹吉他,也不会唱歌,而且她的眼睛是棕色的,个子也不高。"

"可你的妻子温柔漂亮,"朋友说。

"她不但能画出非常美丽的画,而且做饭的手艺堪称一流。"

但是,他却听不进去。

"我真的好难过!"他对牧师说道。

"为什么?"牧师问道。

"小时候,我曾经梦想自己能有三个儿子:一个是伟大的科学家,一个是参议员,另一个是49人橄榄球队的四分卫。结果,我的三个孩子都是女儿,最小的还不能走路。"

"可是,你的女儿都很聪颖漂亮啊,"牧师说。

"她们都很爱你,而且每个人都很出色。一个是护士,一个是艺术家,最小的女儿也能教孩子们学习音乐。"

但是,他却听不进去。

他忧郁成疾,被送进了医院。躺在白色的病房里,身着白色工作服的护士站在他的周围。各种管子和导线把他的身体连到闪烁的仪器上,这些仪器曾经是他卖给医院的。家人、朋友还有牧师都聚集在病床周围,大家都伤心难过。

一天夜里，人们都已经回家了，只有护士还守在他的身边。他对上帝说："上帝啊，您还记得小时候我跟您说过自己长大以后想要的东西吗？"

"那是个美妙的梦想，"上帝说。

"可是，您为什么不把我所想要的东西给我呢？"他问。

"我本来是可以给你的，"上帝说，"不过，我想用一些你做梦都想不到的东西来给你送个惊喜。"

"我猜，你一定注意到我给你的那些东西了：一个温柔漂亮的妻子，一份收益颇丰的生意，一处舒适温馨的房子，还有三个可爱的女儿，这是我所能给你的最好的人生组合。"

"就算是吧！"他打断了上帝的话，"但是，我认为您应该把我真正想要的东西给我。"

"我也以为，你会将我真正想要的一切给我，"上帝说。

"您想从我这儿得到什么呢？"他问。他从来没想到上帝也会有所需求！

"我希望，我所给你的东西能使你幸福！"上帝说。

那天夜里，他整晚都躺在黑暗中，思索着。最后，他决定重新做一个梦，一个他多年前就应该做过的梦。他决定梦想他最想要的正是他已拥有的东西。很快，他恢复了健康，依旧生活在原来的第47层的公寓里，孩子们美妙的歌声悦耳动听，妻子深棕色的眼睛和她那些画有栩栩如生的鸟儿的作品让他陶醉。夜幕降临的时候，他久久地凝视着远方那一望无尽的蓝色海洋和城市中那璀璨闪烁的万家灯火。

A Dream

Anonymous

Focusing on what you have instead of what you want, you'll know what it means to fell satisfied.

Once there was a boy who lived in a big house on a hill. He loved dogs and horses, sports cars and music. He climbed trees and went swimming, played football and admired pretty girls. Except for having to pick up after himself, he had a nice life.

One day the boy said to God, "I've been thinking, and I know what I want when I become a man."

"What?" God asked.

"I want to live in a big house with a porch across the front and two Saint Bernards and a garden out back. I want to marry a woman who is tall and very beautiful and kind, who has long, black hair and blue eyes, and who plays the guitar and sings in a clear, high voice."

"I want three strong sons to play football with. When they grow up, one will be a great scientist, one will be a Senator and the youngest will quarterback for the 49ers."

"I want to be an adventurer who sails vast oceans and climbs tall mountains and rescues people. And I want to drive a red Ferrari and never have to pick up after myself."

"That sounds like a nice dream," said God. "I want you to be happy."

One day, playing football, the boy hurt his knee. After that he couldn't climb tall mountains or even tall trees, much less sail vast oceans. So he studied marketing and started a medical-supplies business. He married a girl who was very beautiful and very kind and who had long, black hair. But she was short, not tall, and had brown eyes, not blue. She couldn't play the guitar, or even sing. But she prepared wonderful meals seasoned with rare

Chinese spices and painted magnificent pictures of birds.

Because of his business, he lived in a city near the top of a tall apartment building that overlooked the blue ocean and the city's twinkling lights. He didn't have room for two Saint Bernards, but he had a fluffy cat. He had three daughters, all very beautiful. The youngest, who was in a wheelchair, was the loveliest. The three daughters loved their father very much. They didn't play football with him, but sometimes they went to the park and tossed a Frisbee except for the youngest, who sat under a tree strumming her guitar and singing lovely, haunting songs. He made enough money to live comfortably, but he didn't drive a red Ferrari. Sometimes he had to pick up things and put them away even things that didn't belong to him. After all, he had three daughters.

Then one morning the man awoke and remembered his dream.

"I am very sad," he said to his best friend.

"Why?" asked his friend.

"Because once I dreamed of marrying a tall woman with black hair and blue eyes who would play the guitar and sing. My wife can't play the guitar or sing. She has brown eyes, and she's not tall. "

"Your wife is very beautiful and very kind," said his friend.

"She creates splendid pictures and delicious food. "

But the man wasn't listening.

"I am very sad," the man said to his minister.

"Why?" asked the minister.

"Because I once dreamed of having three sons: a great scientist,a politician and a quarterback. Instead, I have three daughters, and the youngest can't even walk. "

"But your daughters are beautiful and intelligent," said the minister.

"They love you very much, and they've all done well. One is a nurse, another is an artist and the youngest teaches music to children. "

But the man wasn't listening.

He was so sad that he became very sick. He lay in a white hospital room surrounded by nurses in white uniforms. Tubes and wires connected his body to blinking machines that he had once sold to the hospital. He was terribly, tragically sad. His family, friends and minister gathered around his bed. They were all deeply sad too.

Then one night, when everyone except the nurses had gone home, the man said to God, "Remember when I was a boy and I told you all the things I wanted?"

"It was a lovely dream," said God.

"Why didn't you give me those things?" asked the man.

"I could have," said God. "But I wanted to surprise you with things you didn't dream of. "

"I suppose you've noticed what I've given you: a kind, beautiful wife; a good business; a nice place to live;three lovely daughters;one of the best packages I've put together. "

"Yes," interrupted the man. "But I thought you were going to give me what I really wanted. "

"And I thought you were going to give me what I really wanted. "said God.

"What did you want?" asked the man. It had never occurred to him that God was in want of anything.

"I wanted to make you happy with what I'd given you," said God.

The man lay in the dark all night, thinking. Finally he decided to dream a new dream, one he wished he'd dreamed years before. He decided to dream that what he wanted most were the very things he already had. And the man got well and lived happily on the 47th floor, enjoying his children's beautiful voices, his wife's deep brown eyes and her glorious paintings of birds. And at night he gazed at the ocean and contentedly watched the lights of the city twinkling on,one by one.have than what you want. If you do, your life will start appearing much better than before.

朋友

佚名

真正的朋友是一个可以援手帮助并感动你心扉的人。

经常会有人伤害你,所以你该继续付出信任,但小心挑选你下次信任的人。

在你想了解别人也想让别人了解你之前,先完善并了解自己。

要记住:任何事情的发生都有因有起。

有多少人可以拥有八个真正的朋友?就我所知少之又少。但我们会有泛泛之交和好友。

Friends

Anonymous

A true friend is someone who reaches for your hand and touches your heart.

There's always going to be people that hurt you, so what you have to do is keep on trusting and just be more careful about who you trust next time around.

Make youself a better person and know who you are before you try and know someone else and expect them to know you.

Remember: Whatever happens, happens for a reason.

How many people actually have 8 true friends? Hardly anyone I know. But some of us have all right friends and good friends.

永远的朋友

佚名

别人都走开的时候,朋友仍与你在一起。

有时候在生活中,

你会找到一个特别的朋友;

他只是你生活中的一部分内容,却能改变你整个的生活;

他会把你逗得开怀大笑;

他会让你相信人间有真情;

他会让你确信,真的有一扇不加锁的门,在等待着你去开启。

这就是永恒的友谊。

当你失意,

当世界变得黯淡与空虚,

你真正的朋友会让你振作起来,原本黯淡、空虚的世界顿时变得明亮和充实。

你真正的朋友会与你一同度过困难、伤心和烦恼的时刻。

你转身走开时,

真正的朋友会紧紧相随。

你迷失方向时,

真正的朋友会引导你,鼓励你。

真正的朋友会握着你的手,告诉你一切都会好起来的。

如果你找到了这样的朋友,

你会快乐,觉得人生完整,

因为你无需再忧虑。

你拥有了一个真正的朋友,

永永远远,永无止境。

A Forever Friend

Anonymous

A friend walks in when the rest of the world walks out.

Sometimes in life,

You find a special friend;

Someone who changes your life just by being part of it;

Someone who makes you laugh until you can't stop;

Someone who makes you believe that there really is good in the world;

Someone who convinces you that there really is an unlocked door just waiting for you to open it.

This is Forever Friendship.

When you're down,

And the world seems dark and empty,

Your forever friend lifts you up in spirits and makes that dark and empty world uddenly seem bright and full.

Your forever friend gets you through the hard times,

The sad times, and the confused times.

If you turn and walk away,

Your forever friend follows,

If you lose you way,

Your forever friend guides you and cheers you on.

Your forever friend holds your hand and tells you

That everything is going to be okay.

And if you find such a friend,

You feel happy and complete,

Because you need not worry,

Your have a forever friend for life,

And forever has no end.

如何种植薰衣草

佚名

猜猜哪种植物是紫色的而且闻起来很香呢?你答对了!那就是薰衣草,一种娇小又美丽的花。

我想在暑假时用薰衣草来装饰我的花园,使它变得有生气。首先,我会在花园的四周播种。然后,我会每天浇水。我希望薰衣草快快长大,那样我就可以看到漂亮的花儿了。

当种植完毕,我想送朋友们一些种子。这样一来,我就能跟他们一同分享我的暑假了。

How to Grow Lavender

Anonymous

Guess what plant is purple and smells wonderful. You are right ! It is lavender, a small and beautiful flower.

During my summer vacation, I would like to liven up my gardenwith lavender. First, I will plant some seeds around the garden. Then Iwill water the lavender every day. I hope the lavender will grow up fast so I can see the pretty flowers.

Once I have finished, I want to send some seeds to my friends.This way, I can share my summer vacation with them.

失败者的学堂

佚名

能在紧急时刻迅速做出决断的人并不是天才——因为他们的才华并不出众，可是他们却懂得只有将全部注意力都集中在一处时所作出的判断才是最可取的。许多商界人士所创造的奇迹都不是偶然的。因为他们懂得如何找到新理念，以及攻克难关的法宝。正是这一点决定着世人的成败。成功人士在寻找成功之路时常常抱定必胜的决心。而失败者却总是认为自己一定会失败——正是这种思想导致他们永远不会取得真正的成功。

我认为任何人都可以通过一定的训练取得成功。许多才华横溢的人都没有将自己的潜能充分发挥出来，这不禁使人感到惋惜。我真希望有一天哪位慈善家能够出资兴建一个学校，让失败者聚在一起，教授他们如何能够获得成功。这才叫做把钱花在刀刃上！只需一年时间，这些失败者就能够在学习中增进不少。他们最终会发现，自己之所以失败，完全是因为其意志力不坚强，经常受到悲伤与不幸经历的困扰，致使自己失去了再战的勇气。

失败者首先要做的就是通过努力达到自食其力。可是，想实现这个愿望并不容易，有时甚至会适得其反。如果他们的潜能最终没能被挖掘出来，那么不仅他们会受到损失，这个世界也同样会受到损失。我相信在不久的将来一定会有人乐于出资帮助那些失败者重新站立起来；帮助他们认识到自身拥有的巨大潜能，并将这些潜能用到实处；帮助他们摆脱绝望的情绪，让他们重拾自信。

如果某人在今天失去了一个大好机会，那么他一定会立即找到补救措施使自己找到另外一个机会——这是人的本性。每个人都需要通过自身的努力走上正确的道路，必须学会将注意力集中在一处，使自己在事业上有所成就。有了缺点，只能通过自身努力来纠正，别人除了能够给你带去勇气以外，根本不能为你提供更大的帮助。你所要做的就是重新振作起来，下定决心战胜所有缺点与恶习。

一个人除非身体健康受到了极大的影响，否则任何困难都不能够成为阻碍你成功致富的借口。想战胜困难就一定要培养坚定的意志力。

也许你至今仍生活在困境中，但只要你给自己一个机会，努力培养自制力，那么总有一天你会得到一份比金钱更加宝贵的资产——它可以使你跨过失败的深渊。

地位显赫的人通常都能够克服重重阻隔，从失败中重新站起来。想想那些伟大的发明家吧！在他们获得最终的成功之前曾经历过多少困难啊！他们很少能够得到亲戚朋友的理解，甚至连一日三餐都不能保证，但是凭借着坚定的决心与无畏的勇气一直坚持到实现愿望的那一天。他们这种坚忍不拔的精神造福了全人类。

大多数人都知道自己想要的是什么，但却很少有人为了梦想而勇往直前。他们不肯为了梦想而做出牺牲。要知道，想要获得成功最切实可行的方法就是勇往直前。哪怕是一个一无是处的人，只要下定了决心为梦想而前行，那么他也一定能够获得成功。再大的困难也阻挡不了那些有着强烈欲望的人。正所谓"困难像弹簧，你弱它就强"。如果我们总是能够看到生活中积极的一面，那么我们一定能够战胜一切困难，而勇气就是我们的"战利品"。

不要以为你前行的路上会一帆风顺，事实上你总会遇到暗礁险滩。不要让困难击垮，而要继续前行。任何时候都不要停下脚步去抱怨自己的境遇，而要在心中描绘出一幅美好的前景——也许不远处就是你渴望以久的乐土。

A School for Failures

Anonymous

The man that is chosen at the crucial time is not usually a genius; he does not possess any more talent than others, but he has learned that results can only be produced by untiring concentrated effort. That "miracles," in business do not just "happen." He knows that the only way they will happen is by sticking to a proposition and seeing it through. That is the only secret of why some succeed and others fail. The successful man gets used to seeing things accomplished and always feels sure of success. The man that is a failure gets used to seeing failure, expects it and attracts it to him.

It is my opinion that with the right kind of training every man could be a success. It is really a shame that so many men and women, rich in ability and talent, are allowed to go to waste, so to speak. Some day I hope to see a millionaire philanthropist start a school for the training of failures. I am sure he could not put his money to a better use. In a year's time the science of practical.psychology could do wonders for him. He could have agencies on the lookout for men that had lost their grip on themselves; that had through indisposition weakened their will; that through some sorrow or misfortune had become discouraged.

At first all they need is a little help to get them back on their feet, but usually they get a knock downwards instead. The result is that their latent powers never develop and both they and the world are the losers. I trust that in the near future, someone will heed the opportunity of using some of his millions in arousing men that have begun to falter. All they need to be shown is that there is within them an omnipotent source that is ready to aid them, providing they will make use of it. Their minds only have to be turned from despair to hope to make them regain their hold.

When a man loses his grip today, he must win his redemption by his own will. He will get little encouragement or advice of an inspiring nature. He must usually regain the right road alone. He must stop dissipatings his energies and turn his attention to building a useful career. Today we must conquer our weakening tendencies alone. Don't expect anyone to help you. Just take one big brace, make firm resolutions, and resolve to conquer your weaknesses and vices.Really none can do this for you. They can encourage you; that is all.

I can think of nothing, but lack of health, that should interfere with one becoming successful. There is no other handicap that you should not be able to overcome. To overcome a handicap, all that it is necessary to do is to use more determination and grit and will.

The man with gri and will, may be poor today and wealthy in a few years; will power is a better asset than money; Will will carry you over chasms of failure, if you but give it the chance.

The men that have risen to the highest positions have usually had to gain their victories against big odds. Think of the hardships many of our inventors have gone through before they became a success. Usually they have been very much misunderstood by relatives and friends. Very often they did not have the bare necessities of life, yet, by sheer determination and resolute courage, they managed to exist somehow until they perfected their inventions, which afterwards greatly helped in bettering the condition of others.

Everyone really wants to do something, but there are few that will put forward the needed effort to make the necessary sacrifice to secure it. There is only one way to accomplish anything and that is to go ahead and do it. A man may accomplish almost anything today, if he just sets his heart on doing it and lets nothing interfere with his progress. Obstacles are quickly overcome by the man that sets out to accomplish his heart's

智慧英文励志篇

desire. The "bigger" the man, the smaller the obstacle appears. The "smaller" the man the greater the obstacle appears. Always look at the advantage you gain by overcoming obstacles, and it will give you the needed courage for their conquest.

Do not expect that you will always have easy sailing. Parts of your journey are likely to be rough. Don't let the rough places put you out of commission. Keep on with the journey. Never sit down and complain of the rough places, but think how nice the pleasant stretches were. View with delight the smooth plains that are in front of you.

学会倾听

戴尔·卡耐基

前段时间，我去参加了一次桥牌聚会。可我不会打桥牌，刚好有一位漂亮的女士也不会打，我们便一起聊天。当她得知我曾在汤姆森先生从事广播事业之前，为了帮助汤姆森准备一些有关旅行栏目的演讲内容而特意到欧洲各地去旅行时，便对我说："啊！卡耐基先生。您能不能把您游览过的名胜古迹或美景讲给我听呢？"

我们刚坐到沙发上时，她便告诉我她和她的丈夫前不久刚从非洲旅行回来。

我说："非洲！那可是一个有趣的地方！我一直梦想着能到那片土地去看看，可我只是在阿尔及利亚待过24小时，便再没有去过非洲其他的地方。快给我讲讲吧，你真的去过那些伟大的国家吗？是吗？多么幸运啊！我真是太羡慕你了！请告诉我一些有关非洲的情形吧！"

随后，她绘声绘色地讲了整整45分钟。她根本就没再问我到过欧洲哪些地方和在异地的所见所闻。事实上，她根本不想听我讲旅行的事情，她唯一需要的不过是一个专注的倾听者，好让她借此机会讲述自己曾经到过的地方。

在日常生活中，这位女士不同寻常吗？不，很多人都是这样的。

比如，在纽约一位出版商的宴会上，我曾经遇到了一位声名显赫的植物学家。我以前从未与该植物学家交谈过，只是觉得他有极强的个人魅力。我毕恭毕敬地坐在椅子上倾听，他便滔滔不绝地介绍大麻、改良植物新品种的实验，以及室内花园等 (他还向我讲述了许多有关廉价马铃薯的惊人事实)。我家里也有一个小型的室内花园。他耐心而友好地替我解决了我所遇到的一些疑惑。

就像我所说的，我们是在宴会上，其他十几位客人也一定在场。然而，我却忽略了所有礼节上的规矩，把那些客人全部放在一边，与这位植物学家谈了几个小时。

午夜时分，我向大家告辞后，便离开了。这位植物学家找到宴会主人，对我大加赞赏，他说我是"最富激励性的人"。最后，还说我是个"最有趣的健谈者"。

一个有趣的健谈者?为什么?我几乎没说什么话。如果我不选择改变话题的话，就算我想说，我也说不出什么来，因为我对植物学方面的知识的了解少得可怜，就像对企鹅的解剖一样一窍不通。然而，我却做了这些事：我专注地倾听对方讲话。而我这样做是因为我真的对话题产生了兴趣。他也感觉到了这一点，而这一点显然让他很开心。这种专注地倾听他人讲话就是对他人最好的恭维。

所以，如果你想要成为一个健谈者，那么就要做一个善于倾听的人。如果你想使别人对你产生兴趣，你首先要对别人产生兴趣。提出一些他人喜欢回答的问题，激起他们谈下去的兴趣，使其获得一种成就感。

千万不要忘记，对面那个正在与你交谈的人，对于他自身、自身的需求、以及自身问题的关注程度，远比对你的兴趣高一百倍。一个人对脖子上一颗小痣的关注程度要远远超过对非洲40次地震的关注程度。记得下次你跟别人谈话的时候，做一个好的聆听者，激励对方多谈论自己。

An Easy Way to Become a Good Conversationalist

Dale Carnegie

Some time ago, I attended a bridge party. I don't play bridge and there was a woman there who didn't play bridge either. She had discovered that I had once been Lowell Thomas' manager before he went on the radio and that I had traveled in Europe a great deal while helping him prepare the illustrated travel talks he was then delivering. So she said: "Oh, Mr. Carnegie, I do want you to tell me about all the wonderful places you have visited and the sights you have seen."

As we sat down on the sofa, she remarked that she and her husband had recently returned from a trip to Africa.

"Africa!" I exclaimed. "How interesting! I've always wanted to see Africa, but I never got there except for a twenty–four–hour stay once in Algiers. Tell me, did you visit the big–game country? Yes? How fortunate. I envy you. Do tell me about Africa."

That kept her talking for forty–five minutes. She never again asked me where I had been or what I had seen. She didn't want to hear me talk about my travels. All she wanted was an interested listener, So she could expand her ego and tell about where she had been.

Was she unusual? No. Many people are like that.

For example, I met a distinguished botanist at a dinner party given by a New York book publisher. I had never talked with a botanist before, and I found him fascinating. I literally sat on the edge of my chair and listened while he spoke of exotic plants and experiments in developing new forms of plant life and indoor gardens （and even told me astonishing facts about the humble potato）. I had a small indoor garden of my own and he was good enough to tell me how to solve some of my problems.

As I said, we were at a dinner party. There must have been a dozen other guests,but I violated all the canons of courtesy, ignored everyone else, and talked for hours to the botanist.

Midnight came, I said good night to everyone and departed. The botanist then turned to our host and paid me several flattering compliments. I was "most stimulating." I was this and I was that, and he ended by saying I was a "most interesting conversationalist."

An interesting conversationalist? Why, I had said hardly anything at all. I couldn't have said anything if I had wanted to without changing the subject, for I didn't know any more about botany than I knew about the anatomy of a penguin. But I had done this: I had listened intently. I had listened because I was genuinely interested. And he felt it. Naturally that pleased him. That kind of listening is one of the highest compliments we can pay anyone.

So if you aspire to be a good conversationalist, be an attentive listener. To be in teresting, be interested. Ask questions that other persons will enjoy answering. Encourage them to talk about themselves and their accomplishments.

Remember that the people you are talking to are a hundred times more interested in themselves and their wants and problems than they are in you and your problems.A boil on one's neck interests one more than forty earthquakes in Africa. Think of that the next time you start a conversation. Be a good listener. Encourage others to talk about themselves.

生命的转变

佚名

　　1921年,刘易斯·劳斯成为纽约新新监狱的典狱长。那个时期,新新监狱比其他任何监狱都要粗暴。但是,大约20年后,当刘易斯·劳斯退休时,这个监狱变成了一个最具人道主义的地方。研究过其管理体制的人都认为,这是劳斯的功劳。但问他这种转变的原因时,他只是说:"这一切都要归功于我伟大的妻子凯瑟琳,她就长眠在监狱的围墙外。"

　　当刘易斯当上典狱长时,凯瑟琳·劳斯已是三个孩子的母亲了。一开始,人们都警告她,绝不要迈进监狱的围墙。但那却没能阻止凯瑟琳的脚步。监狱第一次举行篮球赛时,她就带着三个漂亮的孩子来到体育馆,和犯人们一起坐在看台上。

　　她想:"我和丈夫会照顾这些人,我也相信他们会照顾我。我没有必要担心!"她坚持要认识他们并看他们的档案。她发现一个杀人犯是盲人,就去探望他,她握住他的手问道:"你懂布莱叶盲文吗?"

　　"什么是布莱叶盲文?"他问。然后,她就教他如何读盲文。很多年后,他都对她感恩涕零。后来,凯瑟琳发现监狱有一个聋哑人,她就去学校学习一些简单的手语。人们都说,1921年到1937年,耶稣在新新监狱复活了,凯瑟琳·劳斯就是他的化身。

　　后来,她不幸在一次车祸中丧生。第二天早上,刘易斯·劳斯没来上班,代理典狱长顶替了他的位置。所有的犯人好像很快都察觉到出事了。

　　第二天,她的尸体停放在家中的棺材里,距监狱有四分之三英里远。早上,代理监狱长巡视时,惊愕地发现这群最粗暴、最丑陋的囚犯像野兽一样聚集在监狱门口。他走近才注意到他们流着悲痛的泪水,他们是那么深爱着凯瑟琳。他转过身来,对他们说道:"好吧,你们可以去,但是今晚一定要回来报到。"然后,他打开牢门,犯人们排着队走了出去,一个警卫都没有——四分之三英里的路程,竟没安排一个警卫。他们最后一次表达了对凯瑟琳·劳斯的尊敬。

　　晚上,每个人都回来报到了,一个都不少!

Changed Lives

Anonymous

In 1921, Lewis Lawes became the warden at Sing Sing Prison. No prison was tougher than Sing Sing during that time. But when Warden Lawes finished work some 20 years later, that prison had become a humanitarian institution. Those who studied the system said it was because of Lawes. But when he was asked about the change, here's what he said, "I owe it all to my wonderful wife, Catherine, who is buried outside the prison walls."

Catherine Lawes was a young mother with three small children when her husband became the warden. Everybody warned her from the beginning that she should never set foot inside the prison walls, but that didn't stop Catherine! When the first prison basketball game was held, She went into the gym with her three beautiful kids and she sat in the stands with the prisoners.

She thought: "My husband and I are going to take care of these men and I believe they will take care of me! I don't have to worry!" She insisted on getting to know them and their

records. She discovered one convicted murderer was blind so she paid him a visit. Holding his hand in hers she said,"Do you read Braille?"

"What's Braille?" he asked. Then she taught him how to read. Years later he would weep in love for her. Later, Catherine found a deaf—mute in prison. She went to school to learn how to use sign language. Many said that Catherine Lawes was the body of Jesus that came alive again in Sing Sing from 1921 to 1937.

Then, she was killed in a car accident. The next morning Lewis Lawcs didn't come to work, so the acting warden took his place. It seemed almost immediately that the prison knew something was wrong.

The following day, her body was resting in a casket in her home, threequarters of a mile from the prison. As the acting warden took his early morning walk, he was shocked to see a large crowd of the toughest, hardestlooking criminals gathered like a herd of animals at the main gate. He came closer and noted tears of grief and sadness. He knew how much they loved Catherine. He turned and faced the men, "All right, men, you can go. Just be sure and check in tonight." Then he opened the gate and the criminals walked in line, without a guard, the three—quarters of a mile to stand in line to pay their final respects to Catherine Lawes.

And every one of them checked back in. Every one!

工作和娱乐

温斯顿·伦纳德·斯宾塞·丘吉尔

　　要想拥有真正的幸福与平安，一个人至少应有两三种兴趣爱好，而且一定是真正的兴趣爱好。直到年老时才开始提起"我对某事感兴趣"就无丝毫的意义了，此类尝试除了加重精神上的负担外，别无他用。一个人可以从那些与日常工作无关的某些领域中获取渊博的知识，但是，这样几乎不能使他得到真正意义上的益处或放松。由着自己的性子做事并无益处，你应当做到干一行爱一行。从广义上来讲，人类可以分为三类：疲劳而死的人、忧郁而死的人和烦恼而死的人。对于那些体力劳动者而言，历时一周的辛苦劳作后，在周六下午为他们提供踢足球或打棒球的机会则毫无意义而言。而对于那些机关政要、专业人士或者商界精英而言，他们已被一些棘手的事务劳烦了整整六天，到了周末，还要他们为琐事劳神，依然无丝毫意义可言。

　　抑或可以如是说，理智、勤奋又有用的人可以分为两类：第一类人，工作和娱乐有着严格的界限；第二类人，工作和娱乐合二为一，互相兼容。当然，有一大部分人是属于第一类人的。他们可以获得相应的酬劳。经历办公室或工厂里的长时间的工作后，他们得到的不仅仅是赖以生存的金钱，还有一种对娱乐的强烈渴求，即使是最简单、最朴实的娱乐方式。而第二类人则堪称是命运的宠儿了。他们的生活轻松自然、愉悦和谐。对于这类人而言，工作时间从来不显多，每一天对于他们而言都是假期；可是，当正常的假期到来时，他们却感觉自己正在倾心投入的休假被强行中断了，并会因此而抱怨。

　　当然了，仍有一些东西对于这两类人而言都十分必要，那就是改变一下角度，变换一种氛围，卖力地去完成一件别的事情。其实，那些把工作当娱乐的人，需要每隔一段时间以一种合理的方式把工作从他们的大脑中驱逐出去。

Work and Pleasure

Winston Leonard Spencer Churchill

To be really happy and really safe, one ought to have at least two or three hobbies, and they must all be real. It is no use starting late in life to say:" I will take an interest in this or that." Such an attempt only aggravates the strain of mental effort. A man may acquire great knowledge of topics unconnected with his daily work, and yet hardly get any benefit or relief. It is no use doing what you like; you have got to like what you do. Broadly speaking, human beings may be divided into three classes: those who are toiled to death, those who are worried to death, and those who are bored to death. It is no use offering the manual labourer, tired out with a hard week's sweat and effort, the chance of playing a game of football or baseball on Saturday afternoon. It is no use inviting the politician or the professional or business man, who has been working or worrying about serious things for six days, to work or worry about trifling things at the weekend.

It may also be said that rational, industrious, useful human beings are divided into two classes: first, those whose work is work and whose pleasure is pleasure; and secondly, those whose work and pleasure are one. Of these the former are the majority. They have their compensations. The long hours in the office or the factory bring with them as their reward, not only the means of sustenance, but a keen appetite for pleasure even in its simplest and most modest forms. But Fortune's favoured children belong to the second class. Their life is a natural harmony. For them the working hours are never long enough. Each day is a holiday, and ordinary holidays when they come are grudged as enforced interruptions in an absorbing vocation.

Yet to both classes the need of an alternative outlook, of a change of atmosphere, of a diversion of effort, is essential. Indeed, it may well be that those whose work is their pleasure are those who most need the means of banishing it at intervals from their minds.

论抱负

约瑟失·爱泼斯坦

　　如果世界上的每一个人都缺乏雄心壮志，会出现什么样的情况呢？其实并不难想象，也许这个世界会因善的增多而更加和谐，人们少了贪欲之心，少了摩擦与纷争，有足够进行反思的时间；不把工作当作满足个人私欲的手段，而是为集体谋利益的方式；世间的竞争和冲突将永久消除，紧张的生活将成为过去，压力也将烟消云散；艺术不再令人厌烦，它的存在将纯粹是为了行使其庆典的功能；作为社会单位的家庭以及它所带来的精神伤痛也将不复存在；人们也将更长寿，因过度劳累而引发的心脏病或中风导致的死亡将日益减少；人们也将不再生活在焦虑中；时间也将一再延长，因为人们心中不必再怀有某种抱负。

　　哦,那样的生活将是多么空虚而乏味啊!

　　今天,人们总说成功是一个神话,所以抱负更是缥缈。难道是指成功并非一个真实的存在?而成就也只是竹篮打水吗?在星体运转和宇宙事件面前,全人类的一切努力都微不足道吗?显然,并非是成功都值得称道,并非是雄心壮志都应被滋养。一个人,完全可以在很短的时间内培养出自然选择的能力,对值得和不值得做出判断。然而,即使是那些最愤世嫉俗者也会承认成功是实实在在存在的, 成就也有着举足轻重的意义。所谓神话,是存于那些平庸无能者的无用之举。不承认成功的存在,无疑是接受了一种易使人混淆的观点。而暗含在这种观点之中的,是要将一切提高能力的动机连根拔起,将追求成功的兴趣彻底扑灭,将对子孙的关注一并打消。

　　我们无法选择自己的出身,也无法选择自己的父母,更无法选择自己出生的历史时期、国家或成长环境。我们中大多数人都无法选择死亡,更无法选择死亡的时间或条件。然而,我们却可以在这些无法选择的领域中,选择活着的状态:是毫无畏惧地活,还是胆战心惊地活;是光明磊落地活,还是卑鄙无耻地活;是保持对目标的坚定不移,还是做一天和尚撞一天钟。对于生活中的轻重缓急,我们务必要权衡,选择那些使生命绽放光彩的事情,选择决定要做的事,拒绝不想做的事。然而,不管这个世界对我们做出的选择表示怎样的漠视,那些选择也的确都是我们自己做出的。我们的选择是构成生活的不可或缺的因素,而我们的抱负的全部内容恰恰决定了我们命运的构筑。

129

On Ambition

Joserfe Apestan

It is not difficult to imagine a world short of ambition. It would probably be a kinder world: without demands, without abrasions, without disappointments.People would have time for reflection. Such work as they did would not be for themselves but for the collective. Competition would never enter in. Conflict would be eliminated, tension become a thing of the past. The stress of creation would be at an end. Art would no longer be troubling, but purely celebration in its functions. The family would become superfluous as a social unit, with all its former power for bringing about neurosis drained away. Longevity would be increased, for fewer people would die of heart attack or stroke caused by tumultuous endeavor. Anxiety would be extinct. Time would stretch on and on, with ambition long departed from the human heart.

Ah, how unrelievedly boring life would be!

There is a strong view that holds that success is a myth, and ambition therefore a sham. Does this mean that success does not really exist? That achievement is at bottom empty? That the efforts of men and women are of no significance alongside the force of movements

智慧英文励志篇

and events. Now not all success, obviously, is worth esteeming, nor all ambition worth cultivating. Which are and which are not is something one soon enough learns on one's own. But even the most cynical secretly admit that success exists; that achievement counts for a great deal; and that the true myth is that the actions of men and women are useless. To believe otherwise is to take on a point of view that is likely to be deranging. It is, in its implications, to remove all motives for competence, interest in attainment, and regard for posterity.

We do not choose to be born. We do not choose our parents. We do not choose our historical epoch, the country of our birth or the immediate circum stances of our upbringing. We do not, most of us, choose to die; nor do we choose the time or conditions of our death. But within all this realm of choicelessness, we do choose how we shall live: courageously or in cowardice, honorably or dishonorably, with purpose or in drift. We decide what is important and what is trivial in life. We decide that what makes us significant is either what we do or what we refuse to do. But no matter how indifferent the universe may be to our choices and decisions, these choices and decisions are ours to make. We decide. We choose. And as we decide and choose, so are our lives formed. In the end, forming our own destiny is what ambition is about.

秋天的日落

佚名

　　最近十一月的一天，我目睹了一次值得纪念的日落。当时我正在小溪发源处的草地上漫步，度过了灰暗寒冷的一天之后，天边的落日终于涌出云层，放出光明。非常柔和而明亮的曙光般的阳光照在干枯的草地上和树干上，照在山脚下的矮橡树丛的叶片上。我们的身影被长长地拉到了东边的草地上，好像我们是阳光中的微尘。这样的光芒是在这一刻以前我们还没有梦想过的，空气也变得暖和纯净，这片草地一时间宛如天堂。当我想到这并不是难得而不复出现的奇观，它将会在以后的无数个夜晚来临，且都会如此壮观，以后来到这片草地上的孩子们也能够如此的欢快和愉悦，想到这里，景象也就益发显得光辉灿烂。

　　太阳停留在那些荒芜的草地上，所见之处没有一栋房屋，辉煌耀眼的阳光撒在遥远的城市，也许，还撒在一些以前没有照耀过的事物之上———一只孤独的沼泽鹰的双翼变得金黄，一只麝鼠从巢里探出头来，还有一些沼泽中的黑色的小溪，从草地发源，慢慢流过一堆残余的树桩。我们在这片纯净明亮的夕照中行走，衰败的草丛和树叶反射着阳光，如此柔和、和谐的光芒，我从来不曾沐浴在这样一条金色的光的河流中，没有一丝波浪，没有一点呜咽。每一丛树木和丘陵都发出仙境一般的光芒，而我们背后的太阳像一个温柔的牧羊人在傍晚时分引领着我们回家。

　　我们就这样慢慢走向天国，直到有一天，阳光会比以往更加灿烂，照进我们的头脑和心灵，用巨大的唤醒力量点燃我们的整个生命，如此温暖，如此恬静，金黄耀眼，好似秋日岸边的夕阳。

Autumn Sunset

Thoreau

We had a remarkable sunset one day last November. I was walking in a meadow, the source of a small brook, when the sun at last, just before setting,after a cold grey day, reached a clear stratum in the horizon, and the softest,brightest morning sunlight fell on the dry grass and on the stems of the trees in the opposite horizon, and on the leaves of the shrub—oaks on the hill—side, while our shadows stretched long over the meadow eastward, as if we were the only motes in its beams. It was such a light as we could not have imagined a moment before, and the air also was so warm and serene that nothing was wanting to make a paradise of that meadow. When we reflected that this was not a solitary,phenomenon, never to happen again, but that it would happen forever and ever an infinite number of evenings, and cheer and reassure the latest child that walked there, it was more glorious still.

The sun sets on some retired meadow, where no house is visible, with all the glory and splendour that it lavishes on cities, and, perchance, as it has never set before,—where there is but a solitary marsh—hawk to have his wings gilded by it, or only a musquash looks out from his cabin, and there is some little black—veined brook in the midst of the marsh, just beginning to meander,winding slowly round a decaying stump. We walked in so pure and bright a light, gilding the withered grass and leaves, so soffiy and serenely bright, I thought I had never bathed in such a golden flood, without a ripple or a murmur to it. The west side of every wood and rising ground gleamed like a boundary of Elysium, and the sun on our backs seemed like a gentle herdsman driving us home at evening.

So we saunter toward the Holy Land, till one day the sun shall shine more brightly than ever he has done, shall perchance shine into our minds and hearts,and light up our whole lives with a great awakening light, as warm and serene and golden as on a bank—side in autumn.

完美的人生

安妮·萨贝

　　到底什么是完美的人生呢?关于这个问题我考虑得已经很久了。做一个好人并过上永恒的生活又该怎么做呢? 我想答案就是要为真正的你而活，而不是为迎合他人而活。每当我环顾周围时,就会看到太多害怕保持自我本色的人,尤其是像我这个年龄的孩子们。他们担心不受欢迎,担心被忽视,这种恐惧远远大过他们要做个坚强的、有个性的自我的念头。看到人们戴着面具诚惶诚恐地害怕被揭穿,我感到非常痛心。每个人都不想做一个真正的自我,我想我却除外,我想向人们证明,个人是世间最好的礼物,我们都应该因自己的真正面貌而倍感自豪。

　　无论别人怎么说,我的生活目标都是充分挖掘内在的自我。在我看来,完美的人生就是尽可能活得真实。我想探索的是自己内在的各个方面,而非我的外表或智力。我这样强烈的人生理想都是源于家人和身边朋友的支持。我的父母总是让我自由地为自己做出决定,也让我从自身的失败中吸取教训。我会永远感激我的父母,因为是他们给了我机会,让我变成今天的样子。我的独立能力让我成为了一个坚强的人。一个人要想拥有充实的生活,就要为追求自己的梦想而冒险。生活本身是上天的恩赐,无论处境好坏,要让生活过得有意义,全凭自身努力。尽管生活有时会遇到艰难险阻,可是在内心深处保持自己的本来面目却是很重要的。我见过许多同龄人,他们在成为社会一员的奋斗中已经迷失了自我。知道这一点后,我便鼓励自己为保持本色、相信自我而努力进取。我生活中的朋友也不断地鼓励着我。我能感受到他们的关心,他们也看重我这个人;相应地,我也表现出对他们的关心,不期待他们成为别的什么人,但愿能坚持他们的本色。

　　只有凭借自己的努力才能实现完美的人生。不管生活中需要克服的困难有多大,都不能丧失信心。所以,无论别人期待你成为什么样的人,你一定要相信自己。一旦丧失信心,就等于失去了所有。要永远为你自己而自豪。

The Perfect Life

Anne Saab

What is a perfect life? I think of this question a lot. What does it take to be a good person, and to live a life that will never die? I think the answer is living for the person you are, and not for the person others want you to be. When I look around me,I see many people who are afraid of being themselves, especially at my age.Their fear of being unpopular and left out overpowers their dream of becoming the strong and unique people they are. It makes me sad seeing people hide behind masks in fear of being revealed. It seems to me that everybody wants to be something they're not. I want to make a difference and show people that being an individual is the best gift in the world, and we all should be proud of being who we are.

My goal in life is to get the best out of the person I am inside, regardless of the opinions of others. The perfect life for me is a life in which I can live close to myself.I want to explore every aspect within me, not just my physical appearance or intelligence. My strong ambitions for a life like this come from the support I have from my family and friends around me. My parents have always let me be free to make my own decisions and learn from my mistakes. I am forever grateful to them for giving me the opportunity to become the person I am today. My independence has made me a strong person.To live life to the max, one needs to take risks in order to pursue one's dreams. Life is a blessing, and it is up to the individual to make each life worth living, regardless of the situation he or she is in.Although life gets tough at times, it is important to stay in touch with who you are on the inside. I have seen many people at my age who have lost their true selves in the struggle of becoming a part of the world. Seeing this inspires me to work hard at staying myself, and having faith in who I am. The friends I have had through the course of my life have given me courage. They have showed me they care about me, and they appreciate who I am. In turn, I show them that I care about them, and that I wouldn't want them to be anything else but themselves.

The perfect life is up to every individual to achieve. No matter how hard it is to tackle the obstacles of life, one must never lose faith. So whatever people might expect of you, always believe in yourself. One who loses his faith loses everything.Be proud of who you are, forever.

最重要的人生法则

杰西·戈登

我学到的最重要的一条人生法则是："不管生活有多么艰难,我都不能放弃。"我必须继续坚持,想方设法改变不利的处境。我的生活应该是有价值的,我要试着快乐地生活,我必须学会正确地对待不同的生活。任何事都不能放弃,因为不管处境多么艰难,总有人在关心我、爱护我。

我曾经挣扎在大多数人都不会想到的困境之中。很多人只是摇头,根本不愿相信会发生这样的事情。在我想要说给他们听时,一些人只是说好像没那么糟糕,便不愿再听下去了。不过,其实我的确需要讲给什么人听,因为我要是忍着不说,情况会更糟,甚至不可挽救。

现在的生活并不像我以前想的那样毫无希望。当时我甚至不敢确定自己现在还能不能真的活在世上,我甚至因为自己所遭受的罪而对上帝产生怀疑,也开始责怪母亲,为什么总是因为一些该做却没有做的小事,如喂狗之类的事情,而让我们挨揍、受罚呢。有一天,大约3点钟,我忘了喂狗,便被惩罚24小时不准吃饭。

另外一次是在我8岁时,距离圣诞节只有七天了。早上6:00的时候,生父把我和7岁的妹妹叫醒,让我们去清扫院子。院子里都是他的啤酒瓶和垃圾。我和妹妹感觉院子非常干净了,就回到屋里,打开电视机看。这时他走了进来,开始大喊大叫地骂我们,说我们不但懒,而且不听话。他说台阶下边还有一小片纸,因此就不过圣诞节了。那年,我们真

137

的没有过圣诞节。

还有一次是在我9岁时，生父在修理搬运车时，叫我把工具递给他。我不知道他要什么工具，就站在原地没动。他站起来，冲我大叫道："为什么不递给我工具？"我只好说不知道哪件，他就打了我一顿，尖叫着说过去我看到过他修车，看到别人给他递过哪件工具，我就应该知道他想要什么工具。结果是我被关在房间里待了一个星期。

这就是我的生活，大多数人都无法想象的生活。从我会爬的时候开始直到母亲离开，那个家每年都没有什么变化，我只要睁开眼睛，就心怀恐惧。我13岁之后，才有朋友到家里来。从那以后，我可以坦然地问问题，可以与母亲和继父一起吃冰淇淋了。在我13岁前，生父一直是当着我和妹妹的面吃冰淇淋，却不让我们吃一口。不久，我就意识到母亲当初也为她自己和孩子们感到害怕，只是不知道该如何是好而已。上帝终于给了她力量和勇气，使她逃离了苦海。

以前，因为在这样的环境中长大，我的生活态度十分差，无论是对我爱的人，还是陌生人，我完全是一副冷漠的态度。我不但脾气不好，也不尊重权威。而且，我学会了整天坐在那里编造谎言。在我慢慢长大，懂得一切之后，我认识到自己有能力改变，有能力成为一个与过去不同的人。我不必像生父那样，我会善待他人，不发脾气，用和善的态度对待每个人。我已经知道，假如我对人家好，人家也会对我好，同时这也就意味着我有了更多的朋友。

我开始更加友善地对待他人。如今，母亲和一个很好的人结了婚，生活得很美满。我也不再觉得生活很绝望、活着没有乐趣了。我认识到自己很快乐，也为自己没有放弃生活而感到高兴。去年，我第一次在期末报告书上得了4分。现在，我有很多朋友，因为我付出了不懈的努力。我改变了令人绝望的生活环境，并且现在的一切都充满着希望、令人鼓舞。

The Greatest Law of Life

Jesse Gordon

One of the greatest laws of life that I have learned is."I can not give up on life even if the situation is horribly hopeless,"I must goon and live, and try to overcome it.My life has value. I should try to be happy, and I must learn how to deal with whatever life throws at me. I must not give up on anyone, because no matter how hard it gets, someone out there still cares and loves me.

I have been in a situation that most people do not think about. Many people just turn their heads and do not want to believe it exists. Some people, when I try to talk to them, just tell me it is not as bad as it seems, and do not listen. But the truth of the matter is I need to tell someone, because if I hold it in it will just build up and make matters worse.

Life is not hopeless like I thought it was. I was not even sure if I should be here in this world. I even doubted God because of the way I was treated. I started blaming my mother for allowing me to be beaten and severely punished for little things that I should have done, like feed the dog. One day, it was about 3:00 and I forgot to feed the dog. My punishment was that I could not eat for 24 hours.

Another example of this treatment was when I was eight years old. It was seven days before Christmas. At 6:00 a.m. my biological father woke up me and my sister,who was seven, to clean the yard, which was full of his beer cans and trash. My sister and I thought the yard was pretty clean, so we went inside and turned on the television. We were watching the television when my biological father came in and started hollering and screaming and cursing my sister and me. He said we did not listen and were lazy. He said because there was one little piece of paper under the steps, there would not be Christmas. That year we did not have Christmas.

Another example is when I was nine years old, my biological father asked me for a tool while he was working on the van. I did not know what tool it was that he asked for, so I stood there. He got up and hollered, "Why didn't you give me the tool?"I simply said I did not know what tool it was. He hit me and started screaming.He said that I have seen him working on the van before, and someone else had handed it to him, so I should have known what tool he wanted. I got grounded to my room for one week.

My life has been like that, and more than most can imagine, from the day I could crawl to the day my morn left. I was thirteen years old before I could have friends over to my home. I was thirteen before I did not have to be seared when I woke up. I was thirteen before I could ask questions without fear. I was thirteen before I could eat ice cream with my mother and stepdad. My biological father would eat ice cream in front of me and my sister and not let us eat any. I soon realized that my mother was scared for herself and for her kids; she did not know what to do. God finally gave her the strength and courage to get out of a bad situation.

In the past, I have had a bad attitude toward life because of the way I was raised. I treated people bad, those I loved and those I did not know. I blamed it on the way I was raised. I had a short temper and did not respect authority. However, I have learned that I could sit here all day making up excuses. But the truth be known, I have realized that I have the power to change. I have the power to be a different person in life. I do not have to be like my biological father. I can treat others well,and not have a short temper and bad attitude with everyone. I have discovered that others will treat me well if I treat them well, which means having more friends.

I started treating others better. My mother is now married to a great man.Life is wonderful. I do not think life is hopeless and not worth living anymore. I have realized that I am happy, and I am glad that I did not give up on life. Last year, for the first time, I had a 4.0 on my final report card. I now have many friends, because stuck with it. I pulled through a horribly hopeless situation, and things are not hopeless anymore.

自我发现和自我强大的16步

侠名

1. 我们的确有掌控自己生活的能力，不再依赖物质和他人来维护自己的自尊和安全。

2. 我们相信，当我们准备就绪，乐意且有能力敞开心扉，在接受心灵愈合的过程中，一个全新的自我会赋予我们此刻所需的智慧。

3. 我们决心展现真我，完全相信真理的力量。

4. 我们要在这个论资排辈的文化背景中，不断地审视自己的信念、癖好以及依赖性的行为。

5. 我们要将羞愧和内疚的事与他人和全新的自我共同分享。

6. 我们要对自己的优点、天赋和创造力予以肯定和赞赏，不要为了不伤及他人的颜面而掩盖这些优点。

7. 让愧疚、自责顺其自然地发生吧，用实际行动大胆地去爱自己和他人。

8. 列一张清单，写下我们伤害过和伤害过我们的人，并通过道歉和诉苦来减轻苦痛或清除负面影响，当然，我们要以礼貌的方式。

9. 向别人表达爱意和感激的同时，要不断地赞赏生命的惊奇和我们所拥有的幸福。

10. 继续相信现实，对我们每天看到和感知到的一切给予肯定。

11.要及时承认过错,并在恰当时机予以更正,但不要为我们未做过的事道歉,不要掩盖和分析他人的缺点,更不必对其负责。

12.找寻能对我们的智力、观察力和自我价值予以肯定的环境、工作和人群,远离那些无益的环境和有害的人群。

13.采取措施恢复体能,让生活井然有序。减少压力,让生活充满欢乐。

14.寻找心灵的共鸣,培养毅力和启迪智慧以回应内心的召唤。

15.正视生活中的坎坷,把它当作成长中的教训。

16.我们逐渐意识到,我们与万物有着千丝万缕的联系。因而,我们应为人类的和平和生态的平衡做出应有的贡献。

16 Steps to Self–discovery and Self–empowerment

Anonymous

1. We affirm that we have the power to take charge of our own lives and to stop being dependent on substances or other people for our self–esteem or our security.

2. We come to believe that our emerging self will reveal to us the healing wisdom that lives within us all when we are ready, willing and able to open ourselves up to the healing process.

3. We make a decision to become our authentic selves and trust in the healing power of the truth.

4. We examine our beliefs, our addictions, and our dependent behaviour in the context of living in a hierarchical, patriarchal culture.

5. We share with another person and our emerging self all those things inside of us for which we feel shame and guilt.

6. We affirm and enjoy our strengths, our talents, and our creativity, striving not to hide these qualities to protect others' egos.

7. We become willing to let go of our shame, our guilt, and any behaviour that keeps us from loving ourselves and others.

8. We make a list of people we have harmed and people who have harmed us,and take steps to clear out negative energy by making amends and sharing our grievances; both in a respectful way.

9. We express love and gratitude to others, and increasingly appreciate the wonder of life and the blessings we do have.

10. We continue to trust our reality and daily affirm that we see what we see, we know what we know, and we feel what we feel.

11. We promptly acknowledge our mistakes and make amends when appropriate,but we do not say we are sorry for things we have not done and we do not cover up, analyze, or take responsibility for the shortcomings of others.

12. We seek out situations, jobs, and people that affirm our intelligence,perceptions, and self-worth and avoid situations or people who are hurtful, harmful, or demeaning to us.

13. We take steps to heal our physical bodies, organise our lives, reduce our stress, and have fun.

14. We seek to find our inward calling, and develop the will and wisdom to follow it.

15. We accept the ups and downs of life as natural events that can be used as lessons for our growth.

16. We grow in awareness that we are interrelated with all living things, and we contribute to restoring peace and balance on the planet.

富得像国王

佚名

　　大约在930年前,威廉一世征服了英格兰,他拥有财富、权势和无情的军队。尽管以他那个时代的标准,他确实是富得令人咋舌,可他却连一个和抽水马桶类似的东西都没有。没有纸巾,没有坐式割草机,他是如何勉强度日的呢?

　　历史上的富人不计其数,可比起我来,他们却是穷酸至极。我有三层隔离风暴的窗户,大财主们却没有。面对亚历山大大大帝,全国的百姓都会瑟瑟发抖,可他却连散装的猫食都买不到。沙皇尼古拉二世甚至没有一把复式轴锯。

　　比起这些逝去的著名人物,我是如此富有,你一定认为我已经心满意足了吧。可问题是,我像大多数人一样,把自己的财富与这些活着的人作比较:邻居、高中同学、电视人物。尽管法国的君主甚至都没能拥有带玻璃门的冰箱,但这并不能减轻我对朋友霍华德的新厨房强烈的羡慕之情。

　　生活水平确实既没有提高也没有降低。几个世纪以来,人们只是寻找不同的素材来发牢骚而已。也许,你以为,只要没有黑死病,人们就会心情愉快,但是,不,我们还想要个热水浴盆。

　　当然,一个获得幸福快乐的方法是,要认识到,即使是按当代标准,我拥有的这些东西也是很不错的。比起许多投资银行家的豪宅,我的房子是小了点,但是,这些房间我和妻子还收拾不过来呢!

　　此外,要是让未来一、二个世纪的人看,那些银行家上等的精致柜台,会和我家陈旧的佛米卡塑料贴面一样简陋。现在我还不能与邻居相比,但是,等着瞧吧!

145

Rich as a King

Anonymous

William I, who conquered England some 930 years ago, had ealth, power and a ruthless army. Yet although William was stupefyingly rich by the standard of his time, he had nothing remotely resembling a flush toilet. No paper towels, no riding lawn mower. How did he get by?

History books are filled with wealthy people who were practically destitute compared to me. I have triple-tracked storm windows, Croesus did not. Entire nations trembled before Alexander the Great, but he couldn't buy cat food in bulk. Czar Nicholas II lacked a compound-miter saw.

Given how much better off I am than so many famous dead people, you'd think I'd be content. The trouble is that, like most people, I compare my prosperity with that of living persons: neighbors, school classmates, TV personalities. The covetousness I feel toward my friend Howard's new kitchen is not mitigated by the fact that no French monarch ever had a refrigerator with glass doors.

There is really no rising or falling standard of living. Over the centuries people simply find different stuff to feel grumpy about. You'd think that merely not having bubonic plague would put us in a good mood, but no, we want a hot tub too.

Of course, one way to achieve happiness would be to realize that even by contemporary standards the things I own are pretty nice. My house is smaller than the houses of many investment bankers, but even so it has a lot more rooms than my wife and I can keep clean.

Besides, to people looking back at our era from a century or two in the future, those bankers' fancy counter tops and my own worn Formica will seem equally shabby. I can't keep up with my neighbor right now. But lust wait.

秋

佚名

进入深秋,大自然的柔和与日渐增。此时此刻不能不唤起我们对大自然母亲的爱,因为她对我们是如此疼爱!在其他季节里,她并没有留下这样的印象,即使有也是偶然的情况。但是在暖和的秋天,大自然完成了收获的工作,完成了她手边的事务,她就对我们充满了慈爱。她现在有了时间,可以抚慰她的孩子们了。能够生活在这样的季节是一种幸福。感谢上帝能够赐予我们如此的和风,这风就能够让我们满足,因为它有着天堂的抚慰!它拂面而过,就好像亲吻我们的面颊,尽可能地在我们的身畔逗留;但是它不得不离去,因此它慈爱地拥抱着我们,然后继续前行,拥抱它将要遇上的一切东西。风儿吹拂,所经过的地方都留下了上天的祝福。我仰躺在尚未枯黄的草地上,对自己低语:"啊,完美的日子!美丽的世界!仁慈的上帝!"这种感觉也暗示着"永生"吧。假人造物主没有让我们进入天堂享受永生的想法,那又为什么会给予我们如此可爱的日子,以及享受如此美好日子的心情呢?金色的阳光就是"永生"的保证,我们可以从透过天堂的门缝照耀到我们身上的金色阳光看到天堂里面的情景。

Autumn

Anonymous

Still later in the season the Nature's tenderness waxes stronger. It is impossible not to be fond of our mother now; for she is so fond of us! At other periods she does not make this impression on me, or only at rare intervals; but in those genial days of autumn, when she has perfected her harvests and accomplished every needful thing that was given her to do, then she overflows with a blessed superfluity of love. She has leisure to caress her children now. It is good to be alive at such times. Thank Heaven for breath—yes, for mere breath—when it is made up of a heavenly breeze like this! It comes with a real kiss upon our cheeks; it would linger fondly arotmd us if it might; but, since it must be gone, it embraces us with its whole kindly heart and passes onward to embrace likewise the next thing that it meets. A blessing is flung abroad and scattered far and wide over the earth, to be gathered up by all who choose. I recline upon the still unwithered grass and whisper to myself,"O perfect day! O beautiful world! O beneficent God! "And it is the promise of a blessed eternity; for our Creator would never have made such lovely days and have given us the deep hearts to enjoy them, above and beyond all thought, unless we were meant to be immortal. This sunshine is the golden pledge thereof. It beams through the gates of paradise and shows us glimpses far inward.

道谢的快乐

佚名

　　生活中，我们很少会对与自己一起生活多年的人表示感谢。实际上，感谢自己最亲密的人——最容易被我们忽视的人，并不一定要等到周年纪念日。如果说我学会了如何表达感谢，那就是：现在就道谢！当你感受到强烈而真挚的感激之情时。说出感谢轻易就能增添这个世界的幸福。

　　说出感谢不仅能让他人的世界更明媚。也会点亮你的生活。如果你觉得失落、不被关爱、不被欣赏，那就试着去接触他人，也许这正是你需要的一剂良药。

　　当然，有时，你不能即刻表达自己的感激之情。这个时候，不要让自己因窘迫而陷入沉默，一旦有机会，就要在第一时间说出来。

　　从前，有个年轻的牧师，名叫马克·布赖恩。他被派往不列颠—哥伦比亚省一个夸扣特尔印第安人的偏远教区。他被告知，在印第安语中没有"谢谢你"这个词。但是，布赖恩很快发现，这些人格外慷慨。他们习惯用自己的馈赠，同样或者更热情的友善来回报别人的帮助。他们用行动来表达感激，而不是说"谢谢"。

　　如果我们的字典里没有"谢谢你"这个词，我想，我们会不会用更好的方式来表达感激呢?我们会不会更积极、更敏感、更在意地作出回应呢?

　　表示感激会产生连锁反应，在我们周围的每一个人之间传递——包括我们自己。因为，没有人会误解一颗感激之心的旋律，它诗歌一般的韵律会跨越世间的一切障碍，传遍世界的每个角落，它美妙的旋律让上天为之动容。

Thanks for Everything

Anonymous

In our life, we have rarely expressed our gratitude to the one who'd lived those years with us. In fact, we don't have io wait for anniversaries to thank the ones closest to us—the ones so easily overlooked. If I have learned anything about giving thanks, it is this: give it now!   While your feeling of appreciation is alive and sincere, act on it. Saying thanks is such an easy way to add to the world's happiness.

Saying thanks not only brightens someone else's world, it brightens yours. If you're feeling left out, unloved or unappreciated, try reaching out to others. It may be just the medicine you need.

Of course, there are times when you can't express gratitude immediately. In that case don't let embarrassment sink you into silence—speak up the first time you have the chance.

Once a young minister, Mark Brian, was sent to a remote parish of Kwakiud Indians in British Columbia. The Indians, he had been told, did not have a word for thank you. But Brian soon found that these people had exceptional generosity. Instead of saying thanks, it is their custom to return every favor with a favor of their own, and every kindness with an equal or superior kindness. They do their thanks.

I wonder if we had no words in our vocabulary for thank you, would we do a better job of communicating our gratitude? Would we be more responsive, more sensitive, more caning?

Thankfulness sets in motion a chain reaction that transforms peope all around us—including ourselves. For no one ever misunderstands the melody of a grateful heart. Its ruessage is universal; its lyrics transcend all earthly barriers; its music touches the heavens.

智慧英文励志篇

爱情、电话畅想

佚名

爱情就是一部电话,你盼着有人打来,它却总是悄无声息;没有任何准备,它却响了起来。所以,我们经常错失另一端传递的甜蜜情意。

爱情就是一部电话,通常并不是程控的,也不能直拨。一声"喂",并不能让你立刻得到答复,一通电话更不可能让你走进爱人的心田。这通常需要人工转接,而且还要耐心等候。命运是这部电话的接线员,她总是不负责任,还喜欢恶作剧,有意无意地捉弄你一辈子。

爱情这部电话总是很繁忙。当你准备好要全情投入,甚至愿为爱情赴汤蹈火的时候,却发现电话已经被别人占用,迎接你的只是"忙音"。这是永恒的遗憾,世代相传,你不过是又一个为了得到爱情之花而憔悴的人儿。 爱情这部电话机有时很敏感,你一拨就通,一"喂"就有回应。可就因为缺乏挑战、不费气力,你多半会挂断,然后悻悻离去。可你一旦醒悟,为时晚矣,无人为你守候。

爱情就是一部电话,很难把握拨号时机,拨得太早或者太迟都会错失良机。

爱情这部电话并非总与幸福形影不离。多少甜言蜜语由声波传递,可相爱的人一旦常相厮守,电话就没了用武之地。难怪许多相爱的人把婚姻看作是爱情的坟墓。

爱情就是一部电话,第一次使用让你紧张不安、激动不已,不是把话筒拿倒了,就是拨错了号码。等你平静下来,又不知道要打给谁。

爱情就是一部电话,常常串线,而且往往出乎意料。不是你的线路串到别人线路上,就是别人的线路串到你的线路上。两种情况均被称为"三角关系"。还好,这种事情转瞬即逝,不会持续。

Love and Telephone

Anonymous

Love is a telephone which always keeps silent when you are longing for a call, but rings when you are not ready for it. As a result, we often miss the sweetness from the other end.

Love is a telephone which is seldom program–controlled or directly dialed. You cannot get an immediate answer by a mere "Hello", let alone go deep into your lover's heart by one call.Usually it has to be relayed by an operator, and you have to be patient in waiting. Destiny is the operator of this phone, who is always irresponsible and fond of playing practical jokes to which she may make you a lifelong victim intentionally or unintentionally.

Love is a telephone which is always busy. When you are ready to devote yourself to or even ready to die for love, you only find, to your disappointment, the line is already occupied by someone else,and you are greeted only by a busy line. This is an eternal regret handed down from generation and you are only one of those who languish for flowers.

Love is a telephone which is sometimes so sensitive that you are put through by a single dial and responded to as soon as you say "Hello". But, more often than not, you only hang it up and tum away sadly just because of its lack of challenge and effort. Once you realize your mistake, no one is available at the other end.

Love is a telephone, but it is difficult to seize the fight time for dialing, and you will let slip the opportunity if your call is either too early or too late.

Love is a telephone which is not always associated with happiness. Honeyed words are transmitted by sound waves, but when the lovers are brought together, the phone serves no purpose.No wonder that many lovers observe that marriage is the doom of love.

Love is a telephone which, when you use it for the first time,makes you so nervous and excited that you either hold the receiver upside down or dial the wrong number. By the time you've calmed down, you will be at a loss to whom you should make the call.

Love is a telephone which often has crossed lines. And this usually happens to you unexpectedly. Your line will either cross or be crossed. Both cases are referred to as "triangles". Fortunately, all such occurrences are transient.

我想了解你的……

佚名

我对你的谋生之道没有兴趣，我想了解你渴望什么，是否勇于追逐心中的梦想。

我对你的年龄没有兴趣，我想了解你是否会不顾一切疯狂地追求爱情、梦想和奇遇，从而保持活力。

我想了解你是否能欣然承受你我的痛苦，而不是去逃避、忘却、报复。

我想了解你是否能享受你我的快乐；我想了解你是否能尽情舞蹈，让身体的每个细胞都沉浸在喜悦之中，不会扫兴地警告我们要小心、要现实、要记住人的局限性。

我对你讲的故事是否真实没有兴趣。我想了解你是否宁愿让别人失望，也要信守自己的原则；是否宁愿接受背叛的谴责，也要忠于自己的灵魂。我想了解你是否忠诚、是否值得信赖。

我想了解你是否能发现美好的事物，虽然生活不是每日都精彩。我想了解你是否能接受你我的失败，而且依然能伫立湖岸，对着一轮明月喊出："我能行！"

我对你的住所或钱财没有兴趣，我想了解痛苦绝望的长夜过后你能否站立起来，能否为孩子们付出需要的一切。 我对你取得的学历、以前的专业和导师没有兴趣，我想了解，当身外之物一一远去，内心深处有什么能让你坚持到底。我想了解你是否甘于孤独，是否在落寞的时刻确实愿意有人相伴。

All I Want to Know about You

Anonymous

It doesn't interest me what you do for a living. I want to know what you ache for, and if you dare to dream of meeting your heart's longing.

It doesn't interest me how old you are. I want to know if you will risk looking like a fool for love, for your dreams, for the adventure of being alive.

I want to know if you can sit with pain, mine or your own, without moving to hide it or fade it or fix it.

I want to know if you can be with joy, mine or your own, if you can dance with wildness and let the ecstasy fill you to the tips of your fingers and toes without cautioning us to be careful, be realistic, or to remember the limitations of being human.

It doesn't interest me if the story you're telling me is true. I want to know if you can disappoint another to be true to yourself; if you can bear the accusation of betrayal and not betray your own soul. I want to know if you can be faithful and therefore be trustworthy.

I want to know if you can see beauty even when it is not pretty every day. I want to know if you can live with failure, yours and mine, and still stand on the edge of a lake and shout to the silver of the full moon "Yes! "

It doesn't interest me to know where you live or how much money you have. I want to know if you can get up after a night of grief and despair, and do what needs to be done for the children.

It doesn't interest me where or what or with whom you have studied. I want to know what sustains you from the inside when all else falls away. I want to know if you can be alone with yourself, and if you truly like the company you keep in the empty moments.

橡树与苇草

佚名

有一次，橡树对苇草说："苇草，咱们聊一聊吧。我知道你可能会抱怨大自然不够公平。你连一只小鸟都承受不起，一阵吹皱湖面的微风都会让你弯下腰。可我却像高山上的花岗岩一样岿然不动，不仅可以遮蔽阳光，还可以抵御暴风雨。生活对我来讲，就像和风细雨一般；可对你而言，却像暴风骤雨一样。要是你能生长在我的树冠下，我会日夜保护你免受风暴的袭击。而你长在潮湿的堤岸，时时受到风儿的侵扰。唉，我只能说，大自然对你太不公平了。"

苇草回答道："老橡树啊，你真是心地善良呀。你可别为我忧心，比起你，我在风中的危险小多了——我只是被风吹弯了腰，不会折断的。虽然以前你一次次都经受住了狂风的侵袭，但谁也说不准以后的结局，咱们还是拭目以待吧。"

正在这时，天边传来一声惊雷，狂风大作，撼动着橡树和苇草。苇草被吹弯了腰，橡树傲然矗立。狂风更猛烈了，咆哮怒吼着。终于，橡树倒下了，虽然他的枝叶在风中摇摆，但他的根已经伸向了坟墓。

The Oak and the Reed

Anonymous

One time the oak said:"Reed, let's talk. I see how you might say that nature is unfair. Even a wren must be a burden on your stalk and any passing puff of air that corrugates the water's face makes you bow down. Yet in my case, my brow,unyielding as a granite mountainside, not only stops those rays the sun shoots far and wide, but it defies huge tempests, too. Life is a breeze for me, a hurricane for you. If you could spring up here beneath my leafage, spread to shelter everything around, no storm could ever touch your head, for I could guard you night and day. And yet you seem confined to ground that borders humid kingdoms where the winds hold sway. No, nature is not fair to you, I have to say."

"Old oak,"the reed replied,"your sentiments betray a natural goodness. But leave off worrying for me; far less than you am I endangered by the wind—I never break, I merely bend. And though till now your back has weathered every blow the wind has struck, we never know how things will end, we always have to wait and see."

Just then, through the horizon's crack, the worst of all the North wind's awful offspring burst in fury from that howling pack and battered both. The reed bowed low, the oak stood fast. Then doubly hard the wind drew breath and raged and roared till one came down—the one that had well-nigh brushed heaven at its crown, but at its base was rooted in the realm of death.

157

火山女神

佚名

八岁时,我看了一部电影,在一个神秘岛上有一座火山,还有郁郁葱葱的树林,树林中有很多野生动物和食人族。统治这座岛屿的美丽女子是火山女神,名叫彤达拉雅,那是一部制作很粗糙的电影,但对我来说,它却展现了完美的人生——被熔岩浆、嗜血动物和野人追赶,只是为换取自由而付出的小小代价。我极度渴望能够成为火女神,并将这个愿望列入了我长大后想要做的事情之中,还向女友询问火女神的写法是否有两个"D"。

多年后,学校的教育体制在我身上得到了充分的发挥。我成为一个正统、负责、可敬的公民,彤达拉雅已被我遗忘得一干二净。父母非常认可我门当户对的婚姻,随后的二十五年里,我成为了一个好妻子,随后又成为四个孩子的母亲,一名可敬而负责的社会成员。我的生活平静乏味得像一碗燕麦粥。我清楚地知道未来的路——孩子们将会长大并离开家,丈夫会与我白头到老,我们会一同看护孙子孙女。

在我满五十岁的第一个星期里,我的婚姻突然间结束了。我的房子、家具,以及我所拥有的一切都被拍卖了,用以偿还那些我根本不知晓的债务。一个星期内,我失去了丈夫、家庭还有父母——他们拒绝接受家族中出现离婚这样的事情。除了四个年幼的孩子,我失去了一切。我所有的积蓄仅够我在找工作期间租一间廉价的公寓,或者购买五张从密苏里州飞往天涯海角——夏威夷岛的机票。

知情的人都认为我跑到遥远的海岛,并企图在那里生存的想法是在发疯。他们认为我用不了一个月，准会爬着回来。我也担心他们的预料会成真。

第二天，我还是同四个孩子带着不到两千美元的积蓄来到了举目无亲的夏威夷岛。我租了间没有家具的公寓，在那里，我和孩子们只能睡在地板上，并以谷物为食。我做了三份工作——跪着擦地板、向游客们出售澳洲坚果、采集椰子。我每天工作十八个小时，因为每天只吃一顿饭，我的体重减轻了三十磅。恐慌袭击着我，使我蜷缩在浴室的地板上，抖得像个患了炮弹震荡症的士兵。

一天晚上，我独自一人走在海滩上，看到远处乞劳伊阿火山喷出的橙红色岩浆。我一边沿海岸蹚着水，一边欣赏着这世上最活跃的活火山。猛然间，我顿悟到：我岂不是白白浪费了这精彩的一幕。由于过去让我无法释怀，现实让我疲惫不堪，而未来又让我惧怕万分，使我无暇顾及眼前的幸福，更没有意识到自己几乎已经实现了儿时的梦想。现在，该是忘记过去，让梦想起航的时候了。彤达拉雅——火山女神终于到来了。

第二天，我辞去了所有工作，把最后一笔薪水花在了购买艺术用品上，开始做起自己喜欢的事情来。十五年来，我不曾画过一幅画，因为在密苏里州我们只是勉强度日，也根本没有钱买颜料、帆布和画架。我怀疑自己是否还能画，是否已忘记了如何下笔。当我第一次拿起画笔时，手就开始颤抖起来，然而不到一个小时，我就完全沉迷于画布上的色彩之中。我画了一只古老的船只。当我重拾自信时，别人也开始对我有了信心。第一幅画还没来得及装裱，就卖了一千五百美元。

接下来的六年里，我的生活充满了冒险经历。我与孩子们同海豚一起游泳，观看鲸鱼表演，并一同攀登火山口。每天清晨醒来，眼前就是一片大海，身后是令我灵感飞翔的活火山。我四十多年前的梦想如今已成为现实。我居住的岛上不断会有火山喷发。在那儿只有野猪、猫鼬，没有食人族。晚上，我时常能听到当地舞者在海滩上跳舞时敲鼓的声音。

有生以来，我第一次感到如此自由自在。我就是彤达拉雅，火山女神，名字的写法中有两个"D"。从那以后，我一直幸福地生活着。

Fire Goddess

Anonymous

When I was eight years old, I saw a movie about a mysterious island that had an erupting volcanoand lush jungles filled with wild animals and cannibals. The island was ruled by a beautiful woman called Tondalaya, the Fire Goddess of the Volcano. It was a terrible low budget movie, but to me, it represented the perfect life.Being chased by moltenlava, blood thirsty animals and savages was a small price to pay for freedom. I desperately wanted to be the Fire Goddess. I wrote it on my list of things to be when I grow up, and I asked my girlfriend if Fire Goddess was spelled with two"D"s.

Through the years, the school system did its best to mold me into a nononsense, responsible, respectable citizen, and Tondalayawas forgotten. My parents approved of my suitable marriage and I spent the next 25 years being a good wife, eventually the mother of four, and a very respectable responsible member of society. My life was as blandand boring as a bowl of oatmeal. I knew exactly what to expect in the future.The children would grow up and leave home, my husband and I would grow old together, and we'd baby –sitthe grandchildren.

The week I turned 50, my marriage came to a sudden end. My house, furniture and everything I'd owned was auctioned off to pay debts I didn't even know existed.In a week I had lost my husband, my home and my parents who refused to accept a divorce in the family. I'd lost everything except my four teenage children. I had enough money to rent a cheap apartment while I looked for a job or I could use every penny I had to buy five plane tickets from Missouri to the most remote island in the world, the big island of Hawaii.

Everyone said I was crazy to think I could just run off to an island and survive.They predicted I'd come crawling back in a month. Part of me was afraid they were right.

The next day, my four children and I landed on the big island of Hawaii with less than $2,000, knowing no one in the world was going to help us. I rented an unfurnished apartment where we slept on the floor and lived on cereal. I worked three jobs scrubbingfloors on my hands and knees, selling macadamia nuts to tourists and gathering coconuts. I worked 18 hours a day and lost 30 pounds because I lived on one meal a day. I had panic attacks that left me curled into a knot on the bathroom floor shaking like a shell-shocked soldier.

One night as I walked alone on the beach, I saw the red Orange glow of the lava pouring out of Kilauea Volcano in the distance. I was wading in the Pacific Ocean,watching the world's most active volcano, and wasting that incredible moment,because I was haunted by the past, exhausted by the present and terrified of the future. I'd almost achieved my childhood dream but hadn't realized it, because I was focused on my burdens instead of my blessings. It was time to live my imagination not my history. Tondalaya, the Fire Goddess of the Volcano had finally arrived.

The next day, I quit my jobs and invested my last paycheckin art supplies and began doing what I loved. I hadn't painted a picture in 15 years, because we barely scratched out a living on the farm in Missouri, and there hadn't been money for the tubes of paint, and canvas and frames. I wondered if I could still paint or if I had forgotten how. My hands trembled the first time I picked up a brush. But before an hour had passed, I was lost in the colors spreading across the canvas in front of me. I painted pictures of old sailing ships and as soon as I started believing in myself,other people started believing in me, too. The first painting sold for $1,500 before I even had time to frame it.

The past six years have been filled with adventures. My children and I have gone swimming with dolphins, watched whales and hiked around the crater rim of the volcano. We wake up every morning with the ocean in front of us and the volcano behind us. The dream I had more than 40 years ago is now reality. I live on an island with a continuously erupting volcano. The only animals in the jungle are wild boarsand mongooses and there aren't any cannibals. But often in the evening, I can hear the drums from native dancers on the beach.

I'm free for the first time in my life. I am Tondalaya, the Fire Goddess of the Volcano, spelled with two"D"sand I'm living happily ever after.

拥有梦想

佚名

我九岁的时候,住在美国北卡罗来纳州的一个小镇上。一次,我在一本儿童杂志的背面看到一则招聘名信片推销员的广告。我对自己说,我一定能干好这事。于是我恳求妈妈让我叫人去取全套推销品。两个星期后,货物送来了,我一把撕下货物外面的牛皮纸,冲出了家门。三个小时后,我的卡片已经销售一空,而兜里则装满了钱。我兴奋地跑回家,大叫着:"妈妈,所有的人都迫不及待地想要买我的卡片!"于是,一个真正的销售员诞生了。

我十二岁的时候,父亲带我去听齐格·齐格勒先生的演说。至今我仍记得当时坐在幽暗的礼堂里听着齐格勒先生的销售学演说的情景。他把每个人的热情都调动起来了。我离开的时候,心中已经充满激情,似乎什么事儿都难不倒我。上车时,我转过身来对父亲说:"爸爸,我也想像齐格勒先生一样。"父亲问我的话是什么意思。我回答说:"我想做一个像齐格勒先生一样的演说家。"从那天起,我的梦想诞生了。

近些年来,我开始鼓励别人去努力实现自己的梦想。在此之前的四年里,我在一个拥有百家公司的财团工作,从一个销售培训者一直做到地区销售经理,正当我的事业如日中天之时,我却选择了离开。许多人都颇感惊讶,他们无法理解在我的收入已达六位数的时候为何选择离开。他们问我为什么仅仅为了一个小小的梦想就不顾一切地去冒险。

我是在参加了一次公司组织的地区销售会以后,才决定辞去自己原本稳定的工作,去开办自己的公司的。确切地说,是我们公司副总裁的一番讲话,改变了我一生的命运。他问我:"如果一个圣人会满足你三个心愿,那么你希望能够得到什么?"他让我把那三个愿望写在纸上,然后问道:"你为什么会需要一个圣人呢?"那一刻,我永远无法忘记他的话给我带来的震撼。

我已有了毕业文凭、成功的销售经验、无数次的演讲经历。还为一家拥有百家公司的财团做过销售培训和管理工作——所有这一切,都已为我所做的决定做好了准备。是的,不需要圣人的帮助,我也可以成为一位出色的演说家。

当我含泪告诉老板我的计划时,这个我十分敬重的杰出企业家回答说:"勇往直前吧,你一定会成功的!"

刚刚下定决心的我,就遭受了考验。我辞职一星期后,丈夫就失业了。我们最近刚买了新房,需要双收入才能保证还清每月的房屋贷款。可现在我们已沦落到一分钱的收入都没有的境地了。我曾想过回到原来的公司,我知道他们仍需要我,但我也知道,一旦回去,就再不能离开了。于是我决定继续向前,决不做一个只会说"如果……就好了"的人。从那天起,一个演说家诞生了。

我紧紧追随着梦想,甚至在最艰难的时期也没有放弃。终于,奇迹出现了。不久后,我的丈夫找到了一份更好的工作,我们没有拖欠一个月的房屋贷款。我也开始有客户预约演说。我发现了梦想令人难以置信的力量。我热爱过去的工作和我的那些同事,还有我离开的那家公司,但是,我实现梦想的时机已到,不得不离开。为了庆祝我的成功,我请了一位当地的艺术家把我的新房子漆上油彩画,上面的图案是一座花园。在墙壁一侧的顶端,她用刷子写下了这样一句话:"这个世界永远属于有梦的人。"

The Dreamer

Anonymous

When I was nine years old living in a small town in North Carolina I found an ad for selling greeting cards in the back of a children's magazine. I thought to myself I can do this. I begged my mother to let me send for the kit. Two weeks later,when the kit arrived, I ripped off the brown paper wrapper, grabbed the cards and dished from the house. There hours later, I returned home with no card and a pocket full of money proclaiming,"Mama, all the people couldn't wait to buy my cards! "A salesperson was born.

When I was twelve years old, my father took me to see Zig Ziegler. I remember sitting in that dark auditorium listening to Mr.Zigler raise everyone's spirits up to the ceiling,I left there feeling like I could do anything. When we got to the car, I turned to my father and said,"Dad, I want to make people feel like that."My father asked me what I meant."I want to be a motivational speaker just like Mr.Zigler."I replied.A dream was born.

Recently, I began pursuing my dream of motivating others. After a four –year relationship with a major fortune 100 company beginning as a sales–trainer and ending as a regional sales manager, I left the company at the height of my career. Many people were astounded that I would leave after earning a six–figure income. And they asked why I would risk everything for a dream.

I made my decision to start my own company and leave my secure position after attending a regional sales meeting. The vice–president of our company delivered a speech that changed my life. He asked us,"If a genie would grant you three wishes what would they be?"After giving us a moment to write down the three wishes,he then asked us,"Why do you need a genie?"I would never forget the empowerment I felt at that moment.

I realized that everything I had accomplished — the graduate degree, the successsful sales career, speaking engagements, training and managing for a fortune 100 company had prepared me for this moment. I was ready and did not need a genie's help to become a motivational speaker.

When I tearflly told my boss my plans this incredible leader whom I respect so much replied,"Precede with reckless abandon and you will be successful."

Having made that decision, I was immediately tested. One week after I gave notice, my husband was laid off from his job. We had recently bought a new home and needed both incomes to make the monthly mortgage payment and now we were done to no income. It was tempting to turn back to my former company, knowing they wanted me to stays but I was certain that if I went back, I would never leave. I decided I still wanted to move forward rather than end up with a mouth full of"if onlys"later on. A motivational speaker was born.

When I held fast to my dream, even during the tough times. The miracles really began to happen. In a short time period my husband found a better job. We didn't miss a mortgage payment. And I was able to book several speaking engagements with new clients. I discovered the incredible power of dreams. I loved my old job,my peers and the company I left, but it was time to get on with my dream. To celebrate my success I had a local artist paint my new office as a garden. At the top of one wall she stenciled," The world always makes way for the dreamer."

我不懂写作

佚名

十五岁那年,在一次英语课上,我向全班同学宣布说要写一本书,并要自己配插图。半数同学在一旁窃笑,其余的同学已经笑得几乎要从椅子上掉下来了。"别傻了,只有天才才能成为作家。"英语老师不以为然地说道,"而且本学期你有可能只得个D。"满腔的热情却只得到这样的回应,我羞愧得大哭起来。当晚我写下了一首梦已破碎的短诗,并将它寄给了《卡普里周报》。出乎意料的是,我的诗被发表了,并且我还因此得到了两美元的报酬。我是作家了,我的作品被刊登了!我把报纸拿给老师和同学们看。他们仍嘲笑我。"不过是走运而已。"老师说道。即便如此,我还是尝到了成功的滋味。我卖出了自己的第一份作品。这比班上任何同学都强,就算只是一时走运,我也心满意足了。

在接下来的两年中,我成功地卖掉了几十首诗歌、书信、笑话和食谱。中学毕业时,虽然我的平均成绩是C,但我的剪贴簿里已贴满了我发表过的文章。我也再没有向老师、同学或家人提起过自己的写作,因为他们都是无情的摧梦者。如果做人一定要从朋友和梦想之间作出抉择,那么追梦才应是首选。现在,我已有四个孩子了,最大的还没到四岁。每当孩子们进入梦乡,我就会在那台破旧的电脑前敲下一些我的心灵感悟。这次的这项工作一共花了我九个月的时间,这就像孕育一个新生命一样。我随意地选择了一家出版社,因为我从来没听说过手稿箱,所以便将手稿放在"帮宝适"尿不湿的盒子里——这是我惟一能找到的盒子。在附信中我写道:"这本书是我自己写的,希望你们能够喜欢。插图也是我自己配上的。我最喜欢的是第六章和第十二章。谢谢。"我用绳子捆好"尿布箱",然后寄了出去,甚至没有在信封上加盖自己的地址,也没有留下一份手稿的复印件。

一个月后,我收到了一份契约、一笔预付款,以及另一本书的约稿。我的书《哭泣的风》成为了最畅销的书，被译成了十五种语言以及盲文销售到世界各地。白天，我出现在电视的访谈节目中，晚上，则回家给孩子换尿布。为了去领各种奖项，我从纽约来到加利福尼亚、加拿大等地。我的第一本书成为加拿大本土美语学校的必读本。作为一名作家，报酬最少的一年我只得到两美元。还记得吗?那时我十五岁。现在最多的一年我可以挣到三万六千美元。多数时候我每年可以挣到五千到一万美元之间。这当然不足以维持生计，但总比做兼职挣得多，而且与不写相比，每年我可以多挣五千到一万美元。人们问我要上什么大学，得什么学位，获什么资格证书才可以成为作家。我的答案是："什么也不需要。"只是写而已。我不是天才，没有写作天分，也不懂得什么叫写作；我很懒惰，也没经过什么培训，而且与孩子、与朋友在一起的时间远远超过我写作的时间。直到四年前，我才拥有一本字典，那是我用八十九美分从集市上买来的一本韦氏小词典。我用来打字的键盘也是六年前花了一百二十九美元买的。我从不用文字处理器。家里六个人的饮食、清洁、洗衣等工作都包在我的身上。我只能到处挤时间写作。所有的文字都是我坐在沙发上，在黄色的笔记簿上速记下来的。与此同时，四个孩子则边吃比萨饼边看电视。手稿完成了，我就打印出来，然后寄到出版社。到目前为止，我已完成了八本书，四本已出版，三本仍在出版社，还有一本写砸了。对于那些有着写作梦想的人，我想大声地对你们说："相信自己，你一定能行。不要管别人怎么说。"我不懂写作，但我却成功了。写作很简单，也十分有趣，每个人都能做得到。哪怕别人说你不过是一时走运也无妨。

I Never Write Right

Anonymous

When I was fifteen, I announced to my English class that I was going to write and illustrate my own books. Half the students sneered, the rest nearly fell out of their chairs laughing. "Don't be silly, only geniuses can become writers," the English teacher said smugly, "And you are getting a D this semester." I was so humiliated I burst into tears. That night I wrote a short sad poem about broken dreams and mailed it to the Capri's Weekly newspaper. To my astonishment, they published it and sent me two dollars. I was a published and paid writer. I showed my teacher and fellow students. They laughed. "Just plain dumb luck." the teacher said. I tasted success. I'd sold the first thing I'd ever written. That was more than any of them had done and if it was just dumb luck, that was fine with me.

During the next two years I sold dozens of poems, letters, jokes and recipes. By the time I graduated from high school, with a C minus average, I had scrapbooks filled with my published work. I never mentioned my writing to my teachers, friends or my family again. They were dream killers and if people must choose between their friends and their dreams, they must always choose their dreams. I had four children at the time, and the oldest was only four. While the children napped, I typed on my ancient typewriter. I wrote what I felt. It took nine months, just like a baby. I chose a publisher at random and put the manuscript in an empty Pampers diapers package, the only box I could find. I'd never heard of manuscript boxes. The letter I enclosed read, "I wrote this book myself, I hope you like it. I also do the illustrations. Chapter six and twelve are my favourites. Thank you." I tied a string around the diaper box and mailed it without a self addressed stamped envelope and without making a copy of the manuscript.

A month later I received a contract, an advance on royalties, and a request to start working on another book. Crying Wind, the title of my book, became a best seller, was translated into fifteen languages and Braille and sold worldwide. I appeared on TV talk shows during the day and changed diapers at night. I traveled from New York to California and Canada on promotional tours. My first book also became required reading in native American schools in Canada. The worst year I ever had as a writer I earned two dollars. I was fifteen, remember? In my best year I earned 36,000 dollars. Most years I earned between five thousand and ten thousand. No, it isn't enough to live on, but it's still more than I'd make working part time and it's five thousand to ten thousand more than I'd make if I didn't write at all. People ask what college I attended, what degrees I had and what qualifications I have to be a writer. The answer is: "None." I just write. I'm not a genius. I'm not gifted and I don't write right. I'm lazy, undisciplined, and spend more time with my children and friends than I do writing. I didn't own a thesaurus until four years ago and I use a small Webster's dictionary that I'd bought at K-Mart for 89 cents. I use an electric typewriter that I paid a hundred and twenty nine dollars for six years ago. I've never used a word processor. I do all the cooking, cleaning and laundry for a family of six and fit my writing in a few minutes here and there. I write everything in longhand on yellow tablets while sitting on the sofa with my four kids eating pizza and watching TV. When the book is finished, I type it and mail it to the publisher. I've written eight books. Four have been published and three are still out with the publishers. One stinks. To all those who dream of writing, I'm shouting at you: "Yes, you can. Yes, you can. Don't listen to them." I don't write right but I've beaten the odds. Writing is easy, it's fun and anyone can do it. Of course, a little dumb luck doesn't hurt.

做你自己

佚名

幸福不是追求你想要的,而是珍惜你现在所拥有的。

做你自己,不要做别人,当你做的不是自己时,你就不再是你自己了。

在我认识的人中,我所拥有的婚姻绝对是最美好的。

我怎么知道的?其实我不知道,只是感觉。

我的妻子、房子、汽车、身体、孩子、工作、教堂和祖国都让我感到很开心,很幸福。他们当然都有缺点,都有令人遗憾的地方,但他们是独一无二的。

记得一个小男孩曾说过这样一句话:"幸福不是追求你想要的,而是珍惜你现在所拥有的。"真理,绝对是真理。

社会不会适应我们现在所拥有的东西。要不然,我们就不会去买那些更为先进的新版和改良过的东西。我们有了一种感觉,为了让自己开心,我们总需要一些不同的、更好的东西。

世上还有比我妻子更出色的女子吗?或许有。就算我拥有了那个更出色的,那比她更好的还有吗?或许还有。

更好,更别致,更强大,更奢侈的物品总是会有的。即使现在没有,那将来也会有。为了应对现有程序的混乱,电脑程序总需要升级,但升级也往往会导致新的混乱。

虽然现在的我们已经很不错了,但我们还常常想做不一样的自己。因此我们不断尝试着更好、更新鲜的东西。如果你连做自己都不开心,那你还能做谁呢?

做自己我很开心,我不想,也没有能力跟任何一个人交换这个位置。我继续努力着改善自己,带着生活的坎坷,带着一生的差错。我很快乐。

世上富有的人很多,但因富有而幸福的人却不多。这就是关键。你对你所拥有的感到快乐吗?

你对自己感到满意吗?你就是你,这是永远不能改变的。古语说,"做你自己,不要做别人,当你做的不是自己时,你就不再是你自己了。"

It's You

Anonymous

I have absolutely the best marriage of anyone that I know.

How do I know that? I don't, it's just what I feel.

I am happy with my wife, my house, my car, my body, my kids, my job, my church, and my country.

Sure, all of them have snags, all of them have faults, but overall I wouldn't trade them, I am happy.

"Happiness is not having what you want, but having what you have."That's a quote that I remember from a little boy. It's true, very true.

Society doesn't gear us to want what we have. Otherwise, we wouldn't buy the new and improved version. We are made to feel as though we need something different to be happy, something better.

Are there better wives out there than mine? Maybe. Even if there were and I had her, would there then be a better one than that one? Probably.

There is always something better, fancier, more powerful, and more expensive. If not now, it's coming.

Computer programs keep us waiting for an upgrade. An upgrade supposedly fixes all of the current bugs. Often, the upgrade introduces new bugs.

We are in a constant state of trying to get something better and different. We are often trying to be someone different, even when the current us is pretty decent. If you are not happy being you, then who else can you be?

I neither want to nor have the ability to trade places with anyone. I am happy with myself. With all life's faults, with all of my faults and my continuing struggle to improve, I am happy.

There are a lot of others who have more stuff. But there aren't many who are happier with the stuff they do have. That's the key. Are you happy with the stuff that you do have?

Are you happy with yourself ? You are you and that isn't going to change. An old proverb says, "Be what you are, not what you aren't, cause when you are what you aren't, then you aren't what you are."

宽恕

佚名

有一对兄弟,他们住在相邻的两个农场。一天,两兄弟发生了冲突,这次冲突使他们40年的关系第一次出现严重的裂痕。以前,他们一起劳作、共用机械、根据需求来交换劳资,没有出过差错。

后来,长久的协作关系崩溃了。从一个小小的误会发展为严重的分歧,到两人冷言相对,接着就是持续了几个星期的冷战。

一天早晨,约翰家有人敲门。他打开门,看见一个背着工具箱的木匠。他说:"我想找一份活,也许您家哪里有一些零碎活,让我帮您做吧?"

"不错,"哥哥约翰说:"我确实有活可以给你干。望过那条小溪,那边有一个农场,那是我的邻居,其实,那里住的是我弟弟。上个星期,我们之间还有一片农场,后来他开着推土机推倒了大堤,现在我们之间就是一条河了。也许他这么做就是要刁难我,那我就要给他来点更狠的。看到堆放在谷仓旁边的那些木头了吗?我要你给我修一个八英尺高的围栏,这样我就再也不用看到他们的地盘了。总之,我要灭灭他的威风。"

木匠说:"我想我明白其中的状况了。告诉我钉子和挖掘机在哪里,我的工作会让你满意的。"

那天,约翰要去镇上买一些用品,所以他帮木匠准备好了要用的材料之后就走了。木匠一整天都卖力地量尺寸、锯木头和钉钉子。太阳下山的时候,约翰从镇上回来了,木匠也刚好完成了工作。农夫睁大了眼睛,惊讶地合不上嘴。哪里有什么围栏啊,分明是座桥! 桥从这边一直延伸到小溪的另一边。真是一项了不起的工程!

对面的邻居——他的弟弟伸展着双臂从桥上走来,"我做了那么多坏事,又说了你那么多坏话,你还能修建这样一座桥,你真是个了不起的人! "

两兄弟在桥上相见,开心地紧紧握着对方的手。他们回过头看着木匠,他正背起工具箱,"不要走,请等一下。再住些日子吧,我还有很多活要你做。"哥哥说道。"我也愿意留下,但是还有很多桥等着我去修呢。"木匠回答说。

Forgiveness

Anonymous

There were two brothers who lived on adjoining farms fell into conflict. It was the first serious rift in 40 years of farming.Side by side, sharing machinery, and trading labor and goods as needed, without a hitch.

Then the long collaboration fell apart. It began with a small misunderstanding and it grew into a major difference. Finally it exploded into an exchange of bitter words followed by weeks of silence.

One morning there was a knock on John's door. He opened it to find a man with a carpenter's toolbox."I'm looking for a few days work,"he said,"Perhaps you would have a few small jobs here and there. Could I help you?"

"Yes,"said the older brother,"I do have a job for you. Look across the creek at that farm That's my neighbor, in fact, it's my younger brother. Last week there was a meadow between us and he took his bulldozer to the fiver levee and now there is a creek between us. Well, he may have done this to spite me, but I'll get him one better. See that pile of lumber curing by the barn? I want you to build me a fence, an 8-foot fence, so I won't need to see his place anymore. Cool him down, anyhow."

The carpenter said,"I think I understand the situation. Show me the nails and the post-hole digger and I'll be able to do a job that pleases you."

The older brother had to go to town for supplies, so he helped the carpenter get the materials ready and then he was off for the day. The carpenter worked hard all that day measuring,sawing, nailing. About sunset when the farmer returned, the carpenter had just finished his job. The farmer's eyes opened wide,his jaw dropped. There was no fence there at all. It was a bridge,a bridge stretching from one side of the creek to the other！ A fine piece of work！ The neighbor, his younger brother, was coming across, his hand outstretched,"You are quite a fellow to build this bridge after all I've said and done."

The two brothers met at the middle of the bridge, taking each other's hand. They turned to see the carpenter hoisting his toolbox on his shoulder."No, wait！ Stay a few days. I've a lot of other projects for you,"said the older brother."I'd love to stay on,"the carpenter said, "but I have so many more bridges to build."

清理你的精神空间

佚名

回想一下你上一次产生的消极情绪,如压抑、气愤或受挫。当你身处那种消极的情绪中时,你的头脑中在想什么?是混乱如麻吗?还是瘫痪了,不能再进行思考?

下一次,当你发现自己非常压抑,或极其愤怒、万分沮丧时,尽管停止。对!就是停止。无论你现在正做着什么,停止手头的工作,静坐一会儿。静坐的同时,把自己完全沉浸在消极的情绪之中。

让那种情绪完全地将你吞噬,让自己有一点时间真实地去感受那种情绪。在这里,不要自己欺骗自己。用整整的一分钟——仅仅一分钟——不去做其他任何事情,只去感受那种情绪。

当整整一分钟过去,问问你自己:"在今天剩余的时间里,我愿意继续这种消极的情绪吗?"只要你彻底地将自己沉入这种情绪,并真实地去体会它,你就会意外地发现那种情绪很快就消失了。

如果你觉得有必要再将这种情绪继续一段时间,那好,没关系。再给自己一分钟,去体会它。

如果你觉得体会得很透彻了,那就问问自己是否愿意让这种消极继续在你剩余的时间里存在。如果不,那就深呼吸一次,将所有的消极随着你的呼吸释放出去。

这种方法看似简单——几乎是过分的简单了,但是其效果却很显著。通过给自己真正体会消极情绪的空间,你能够真正地去与这种情绪接触,而不是去压抑它、回避它。给这种情绪一定的空间,给它必要的关注,这样就能真正地使你消解了其势力。当你在这种情绪中沉没时,就会明白它只是一种情感,就会不再受其影响。然后,你就可以清理自己的头脑,继续自己的工作了。

试试这种方法。下一次当你处于消极的情绪之中时,让自己有体会这种情绪的一点空间,然后看看随后会发生什么。随身带着一张写着下面这些话的纸:

停止。让自己在这种情绪中沉浸一分钟。我想要这种情绪继续下去吗?深呼吸,放松,继续行动!

这张纸会提醒你要做的步骤。需要牢记的是,用必要的时间真正将自己沉浸于那种情绪之中。然后,当你认为自己充分体会情绪时,就将其释放——让它真正地从你的心中消失。你一定会惊讶于摆脱消极情绪和着手工作的迅速。

Clear Your Mental Space

Anonymous

Think about the last time you felt a negative emotion — like stress, anger, or frustration. What was going through your mind as you were going through that negativity? Was your mind cluttered with thoughts? Or was it paralyzed, unable to think?

The next time you find yourself in the middle of a very stressful time, or you feel angry or frustrated, stop. Yes, that's right, stop. Whatever you're doing, stop and sit for one minute. While you're sitting there, completely immerse yourself in the negative emotion.

Allow that emotion to consume you. Allow yourself one minute to truly feel that emotion. Don't cheat yourself here. Take the entire minute — but only one minute — to do nothing else but feel that emotion.

When the minute is over, ask yourself, "Am I willing to keep holding on to this negative emotion as I go through the rest of the day?"

Once you've allowed yourself to be totally immersed in the emotion and really feel it, you will be surprised to find that the emotion clears rather quickly.

If you feel you need to hold on to the emotion for a little longer, that is Ok. Allow yourself another minute to feel the emotion.

When you feel you've had enough of the emotion, ask yourself if you're willing to carry that negativity with you for the rest of the day. If not, take a deep breath. As you exhale, release all that negativity with your breath.

This exercise seems simple — almost too simple. But, it is very effective. By allowing that negative emotion the space to be truly felt, you are dealing with the emotion rather than stuffing it down and trying not to feel it. You are actually taking away the power of the emotion by giving it the space and attention it needs. When you immerse yourself in the emotion, and realize that it is only emotion, it loses its control. You can clear your head and proceed with your task.

Try it. Next time you're in the middle of a negative emotion,give yourself the space to feel the emotion and see what happens.Keep a piece of paper with you that say the following:

Stop. Immerse for one minute. Do I want to keep this negativity? Breath deep, exhale, release. Move on!

This will remind you of the steps to the process. Remember,take the time you need to really immerse yourself in the emotion.Then, when you feel you've felt it enough, release it — really let go of it. You will be surprised at how quickly you can move on from a negative situation and get to what you really want to do!

时间，一种有限的资源

佚名

美国人认为时间是一种有限的资源，所以他们尽量爱惜它，用好它。美国人经常参加有关利用时间的讨论会或阅读这方面的书籍。他们似乎都希望能把自己的时间安排得更好。专业人士随身带着袖珍记事本(有些是电子记事本)，以便随时留意约会时间和工作期限。人们想尽办法要在有限的时间内挤出更多的生活内容。早期的美国英雄本杰明·富兰克林将这种观念表达得最为透彻："你热爱生命吗？如果热爱就不要浪费时间，因为生命即是由时间组成的。"

对美国人来说，守时是一种尊重他人时间的表现。通常若约会迟到超过10分钟，就应该向对方道歉或解释原因。

在外人看来，美国人似乎受制于时钟，其他文化背景的人则更看重人际关系而非时间表。在这些社会中，人们不会设法去控制时间，而是去感受认识它。举例来说，很多东方文化把时间视为一个周期。从季节的更替到每月月亮圆缺的变化，这些大自然的节奏形成了他们对事物的看法。人们学会去适应环境的变化，因此他们比美国人更易"顺应潮流"，而美国人则喜欢将计划固定好不要更动。

Time,a Limited Resource

Anonymous

Because Americans believe time is a limited resource, they try to conserve and manage it. People in the USA often attend seminars or read books on time management. It seems they all want to organize their time better. Professionals carry around pocket planners — some in electronic form — to keep track of appointments and deadlines. People do all they can to squeeze more life out of their time. The early American hero Benjamin Franklin expressed this view best:"Do you love life? Then do not waste time, for that is the stuff life is made of."

To Americans, punctuality is a way of showing respect for other people's time. Being more than 10 minutes late to an appointment usually calls for an apology, and maybe an explanation.

To outsiders, Americans seem tied to the clock. People in other cultures value relationships more than schedules. In these societies, people don't try to control time, but to experience it.Many eastern cultures, for example, view time as a cycle. The rhythm of nature — from the passing of the seasons to the monthly cycle of the moon —shapes their view of events. People learn to respond to their environment. As a result, they find it easier to"go with the flow"than Americans,who like plans to be fixed and unchangeable.

不要沉湎于痛苦中

佚名

　　一些人的所思所想及该如何生活都受到客观世界和问题的限制。是的,有些人就是喜欢沉湎于痛苦中。但是如果知道了真理,那应该而且也可以做到反其道而行之。你自身有力量改变你的世界,把问题抛置身后,勇往直前。

　　具有讽刺意味的是,这种力量正是来自你视为困难和挫折的事情。这一道理许多人尚不明白。你经历的每一个挫折都会伴有等同的甚至是更大的幸运。你也许没有意识到这点,但你的努力会使你变得日渐出色。你所需要的就是睁开双眼看清楚。

　　来自你奋斗中的幸运有时是隐藏着的,通常你必须长时间地寻找,努力地寻找。但在最终找到时,在历数你的种种幸运时,你会发现一个古老的秘密,一个难以否认的真理,而它似乎逃避了大多数人的双眼。

　　这一秘密极为简单:你越数你的幸运,越多的幸运就会降临到你的头上。

　　被确诊患有癌症的年轻人决心用自己的经历告诫他人早期检查的重要性。儿子需要换肾的那对夫妇决意投身公益活动去鼓励他人签署捐献卡。失去丈夫的女士决定志愿继续她丈夫在社区留下的工作来缅怀他。丢掉工作的那位男士决定利用这一机会做他一直想要做的事情——写本他已考虑数年的书。

Don't Wallow in Misery

Anonymous

Some people let the world and the problems they face dictate what they think and how they live their lives. And yes, some people just love to wallow in misery. But if the truth be known, it should and can be the opposite. You have the power within you to change your world and put your problems behind you as you move forward.

Ironically , the power to do that comes from the very things you see as problems and setbacks. That's what most people don't understand. For every setback you experience there is an equal or greater blessing that accompanies it. You may not realize this, but your struggles are allowing you to become a better person each and every day. You just have to open your eyes and see it.

The blessing that come from your struggles are sometimes hidden and many times you have to look long and hard. But by finding them in due course, and by counting those blessings, you will discover a secret of the ages, an undeniable truth, which seems to have escaped most of humanity.

That secret is very simple: The more you count your blessings, the more blessings are bestowed upon you. ·

The young man who was diagnosed with cancer was determined to use his experience to educate others on the importance of early detection. The couple with a son who needed a kidney transplant dedicated themselves to the campaign to encourage others to sign donor cards. The woman who had lost her husband decided to carry on his memory by volunteering to pick up where her husband had left off in his community work. The man who had lost his job,told himself that he would use this opportunity to do what he had always wanted to do — write a book that he had been thinking about for years.

"双面神"恍然大悟

佚名

　　一位哲学家在古罗马的废墟里发现了一尊双面神像。由于从来没见过这样的神像，哲学家便好奇地问他："你是什么神啊，为什么有两张面孔？"

　　神像回答："我的名字叫双面神。我可以一面回视过去，吸取教训；一面展望未来，充满希望。"

　　哲学家又问："那么现在呢？最有意义的现在，你注意了吗？"

　　"现在！"神像一愣，"我只顾着过去和将来，哪还有时间管现在？"

　　哲学家说："过去的已经过去了，将来的还没有来到，我们惟一能把握的就是现在；如果无视现在，那么即使你对过去未来都了如指掌，那又有什么意义呢？"

　　神像听后，恍然大悟，失声痛哭起来："你说得没错，就是因为我没抓住现在，所以古罗马城才成为历史，我自己也被人丢在了废墟里。"

The Double Faced God, Awakened to the Truth

Anonymous

A philosopher found a statue of double faced God in the ruins of Rome. As it was the first time he had seen such an image, he asked curiously, "What god are you? Why do you have double faces?"

The god answered, "I am Double Faced God. I look back to the past with one face to learn lessons and look forward to the future with another full of hope."

The philosopher asked again, "What about the present, the most significant present? Have you paid any attention to it?"

"The present! "the god was taken aback. "How could I spare a minute to it since I am so busy with the past and the future?"

"The past is gone," said the philosopher, "while the future is yet to come. What we can grasp is the present; if you ignore the present, your knowledge about the past and future will be meaningless however great it is! "

The god, suddenly awakened to the truth, burst out crying, "How correct your comment is! It was precisely because I didn't grasp the present that the ancient city of Rome was turned into a page of history while I myself was thrown into the ruins."

魔枕

佚名

情人节到了，与往常一样，我的日程表安排得满满的。

我的丈夫罗伊是一个很浪漫的人，他策划了一个我们从未经历过的约会，在一家高档餐馆订了位子；爱意浓浓的日子到来的前几天，他还把一份包装精美的礼品放到了我的梳妆台上。

一天繁忙的工作结束后，我匆匆赶回家，一头扎进浴室。等老公回来时，我已把最漂亮的衣服穿好，只等出发了。他拥抱了我，这时来照看孩子的人也刚好到。我们俩都非常高兴。

遗憾的是，我们家里最小的成员却不高兴。

"爸爸。你不是说要带我去给妈妈买礼物的吗?"8岁的女儿贝姬边说边沮丧地朝沙发走去，坐在那位临时来照顾她的女士身边。

罗伊看了一下手表，他知道如果我们想按时到达预订的餐馆，必须马上动身。他甚至都抽不出几分钟时间带女儿到街角的小店买盒鸡心形巧克力。

"对不起，今天回来晚，没时间了，宝贝。"他说。

"没关系，"贝姬回答，"我知道。"

这是一个甜蜜的夜晚，却也有几分苦涩。我总会情不自禁地想起贝姬流露出的失望眼神。想起房门在我们身后关闭的那一刹那，贝姬原本因情人节而兴奋的小脸蛋上的光芒一下子消失的情形。她想让我知道她有多爱我。或许她并没有意识到，我心里已经很清楚了。

如今,那个漂亮的盒子里装了什么礼物我已不记得,虽然我因它兴奋了好几天,但那晚回到家时收到的另一份特殊礼物,却令我永生难忘。

贝姬在沙发上睡着了,手里还拿着一个盒子,放在她的小腿上。我吻了吻她的脸颊,她醒了。"妈妈,我要给您一样东西。"说着,小脸蛋堆满了灿烂的笑容。

小盒子用报纸包着。我撕开报纸,打开盒子,看到了我收到过的一份最甜美的情人节礼物。

在我和丈夫离开家去约会后,贝姬便忙开了。她把我的织品和十字绣盒子都翻出来,先在一块红布上绣好"我爱你"三个字,然后把布料剪成心形,再把剪下来的两块布缝合到一起,缀上一圈花边,最后再往里面塞满棉花。一个心形的枕头做成了。这个枕头倾注了她多少的爱啊! 我会永远珍爱它。

大约13年过去了,那件珍贵的情人节礼物依然放在我卧室的一个特殊位置。女儿已经长大成人,这期间我无数次将枕头紧紧贴在心窝。我不知道这个枕头是否藏有许多魔力,但我肯定,这么多年来它给我带来了无尽的喜悦。女儿离开我进入大学时,它伴我度过无数个不眠之夜。我珍爱这份礼物。更珍爱这美好的记忆。

我知道自己确实是位幸运的母亲,有这么一个值得称道的可爱女儿,她是那么渴望与我分享她心中的爱! 在我有生之年,对我来说,应该不会再有比这更特殊的情人节了。

Magic Pillow

Anonymous

Valentine's Day had arrived and like other day of the year, I was very busy.

My romantic husband, Roy, planned a date like we had never had before. A reservation at an expensive restaurant was made. A beautifully wrapped present had been sitting on my dresser for a few days prior to the heart-filled holiday.

After a hard day at work, I hurried home, ran into the house and jumped into the shower. When my sweetheart arrived, I was dressed in my finest outfit and ready to go. He hugged me, just as the sitter arrived. We were both excited.

Unfortunately, the littlest member in our household wasn't so happy.

"Daddy, you were going to take me to buy Mamma a present, "Becky, my eight-year-old daughter said, as she sadly walked over to the couch and sat down beside the babysitter.

Roy looked at his watch and realized that if we were to make our reservations, we had to leave right away. He didn't even have a few minutes to take her to the corner drugstore, to buy a heart-shaped box of chocolate candy. "I'm sorry, I was late getting home, honey, "he said.

"That's ok, "Becky replied. "I understand."

The entire evening was bittersweet. I couldn't help being concerned about the disappointment in Becky's eyes. I remembered how the joyful Valentine's Day glow had left her face, just before the door closed behind us. She wanted me to know how much she loved me. She didn't realize it, but I already knew it very well.

Today, I can't remember what was wrapped in that beautiful box, which I swooned over for several days, but I'll never forget the special gift, which I received when we arrived, back home.

Becky was asleep on the couch, clutching a box, which was sitting on her lap. When I kissed her cheek, she awoke. "I've got something for you, Mamma," she said, as a giant smile covered her tiny face.

The little box was wrapped in newspaper. As I tore the paper off and opened the box, I found the sweetest Valentine gift that I have ever received. After Roy and I left for our date, Becky got busy. She raided my fabric and crossstitch box. She stitched the words "I Love Ya" on a piece of red fabric, cut the fabric in the shape of a heart, stitched the two pieces together, adorned it with lace and stuffed it with cotton. It was a heart-shaped pillow, filled with love, which I'll cherish forever.

My wonderful Valentine gift has a special place in my bedroom today, some thirteen years later. As she was growing up into a young woman, many times I held that pillow close to my heart. I don't know if a pillow can hold magic, but this pillow has surely held a great deal of joy for me over the years. It has helped me through several sleepless nights since she left home for college. I not only cherish the gift, but the memory, as well.

I know that I am a very lucky mother, indeed, to have such a wonderful little girl, who wanted so desperately to share her heart with me. As long as I live, there will never be another Valentine's Day, which will be any more special to me.

金光小屋

佚名

　　山坡上有一所简陋的小房子,里面住着一个小女孩。小时候,她经常在房前的小花园里玩,隔着篱笆,她能看见山谷那边高高的山坡上坐落着一栋漂亮的房子——有着闪闪发光的金色窗子,小女孩梦想将来长大后也能住进着金色窗子的屋子里。而不再住这么简陋的房子。

　　虽然小女孩爱她的父母和她的家,但还是渴望拥有那样一栋金灿灿的房子,每天都梦想着住在那里,会是多么美好和新奇。

　　她长大了,拥有了能够走出花园篱笆的技能和判断力,走出花园篱笆时,她问母亲能否让她沿小路多骑一会儿车。在女儿的再三恳求下,母亲终于同意了,但只允许她在家附近转转,坚决不准她绕得太远。那天天气非常好,小姑娘直奔目的地!沿着小路,穿过山谷,来到了向往已久的金色小屋。

　　她跳下车子,把它放在门前的柱子旁,注意力集中在通往房子的小路上,目光沿小路继续向前,最终落到小房子上……失望顿时袭上心头,因为她所看到的窗子都是那么普通,而且脏兮兮的,根本就不发光,俨然一座废弃的房子。

　　她非常伤心,不愿再前进一步,便转过身去骑自行车……不经意间,她抬头瞥见了一幅令她吃惊的景象……在山谷的那边也有一座小房子——它的窗子也是金光闪闪的……是她那普通的小屋在太阳的照耀下闪着金光呢。

　　她猛然意识到,原来自己一直住在金色的房子里,在那里她得到了所有的爱,这使她的家成了"金光小屋"。一切她所梦想的原来就在眼前!

The House with the Golden Windows

Anonymous

The little girl lived in a small, very simple, poor house on a hill and as she grew she would play in the small garden and as she grew she was able to see over the garden fence and across the valley to a wonderful house high on the hill—and this house had golden windows, so golden and shining that the little girl would dream of how magic it would be to grow up and live in a house with golden windows instead of an ordinary house like hers.

And although she loved her parents and her family, she yearned to live in such a golden house and dreamed all day about how wonderful and exciting it must feel to live there.

When she got to an age where she gained enough skill and sensibility to go outside her garden fence, she asked her mother if she could go for a bike ride outside the gate and down the lane. After pleading with her, her mother finally allowed her to go, insisting that she kept close to the house and didn't wander too far. The day was beautiful and the little girl knew exactly where she was heading! Down the lane and across the valley, she rode her bike until she got to the gate of the golden house across on the other hill.

As she dismounted her bike and leaned it against the gate post, she focused on the path that led to the house and then on the house itself...and was so disappointed as she realized all the windows were plain and rather dirty, reflecting nothing other than the sad neglect of the house that stood derelictly.

So sad she didn't go any further and turned, heart broken as she remounted her bike...As she glanced up she saw a sight to amaze her... there across the way on her side of the valley was a little house and its windows glistened golden... as the sun shone on her little home.

She realized that she had been living in her golden house and all the love and care she found there was what made her home the "golden house." Everything she dreamed was right there in front of her nose!

智慧英文励志篇

埃玛的鸭子们

保罗·卡勒

1966年,冬天以迅猛之势袭击了我们位于纽约北部的大学,这是几十年来从未见过的。接连三天,暴风雪盘旋翻腾,将整个校园困在大雪之中,阻断了与外界的联系。校园里,到处是迷了路的学生,他们排成一队与恶劣的天气抗争着,就像躲在妈妈身后的小鸭子横过马路一样。与全校师生一样,B寝室的女生们也遇到了同样的问题。

一个女生问道:"我们怎样才能到自助食堂呢?"

另一个女生答道:"我们不要去了。外面白茫茫的一片,什么也看不见。"

第三个女生的眼睛一亮,"嘘"了一声,室内的抱怨声便停止了。然后,她兴奋地说道:"埃玛能够看得见。"

抱怨声消失了,接着是一阵兴奋的低语声。"埃玛!她甚至能够在整个大学城穿梭。""我们可以跟着她走。""你真是一个天才呀!"女生们非常高兴,她们笑语欢声,鼓起掌来。女生们穿戴好,一群人激动地朝埃玛的房间走去。她们在楼道中发现了埃玛,在她打开寝室的门之前,这群女生就把她围了起来。

埃玛笑着问:"你们为什么都这么兴奋?"

"我们能不能跟着你去自助食堂?我们在暴风雪中什么都看不到。"

"我认为可以。我先走,你们排成一列搭着肩膀跟在我后面。"

一个女生恳求道:"我们现在可以出发了吗?我饿坏了。"

埃玛又笑了,说道:"没问题,我们带上密斯一起去。"

她进了寝室,过了一会儿,牵出一条狗。这群女生在门口乖乖地排起了一列长队,准备迎战外面的寒冷。每个人都把手放在了前面女生的肩膀上。

埃玛打开了大门,把大家领了出来。她笑着说:"我猜,你们可以把这个称为盲人给正常人引路。"

说完,埃玛和导盲犬密斯带领着这群饥饿的鸭子朝自助食堂走去。

Emma's Ducks

Paul Karrer

The winter of 1966 hit our university in upstate New York with a ferocity unrivaled in decades.For three days straight,the snow swirled and billowed,burying the isolated campus. Here and there strayed groups of students struggling single file against the weather,like ducklings following their mother across a road.

The female students in dormitory B were confronted with the same problem plaguing the general population of the university.

"How are we going to get to the cafeteria?"asked one."We're not,"answered another. "Everything out there is white.You can't see anything."

A gleam came into the eye of the third girl.She shushed the others' whining,saying triumphantly,"Emma could do it."

The whining turned to murmrs of excitement."Emma! She even manages through the city.""We could follow her.""You're a genius! "

The girls whooped,yelled and clapped for joy.They bundled up and excitedly trooped down the hall to Emma's room,They found her in the hallway and cornered her before she could even open her door.

"What's all the excitement?"she asked,smiling.

"Can we follow you to the,cafeteria? We're blind in this storm."

They all laughed.

"I suppose so. I'll go first, and you could hold on to each other's shoulders."

"Can we go now?" one girl begged. "I'm starving."

Emma smiled again. "Sure, let me just get Missy ready."

She went into her room and returned moments later with a dog on a harness. The girls lined up obediently at the front door, ready to face the cold. They each placed their hands on the shoulders of the girl in front of them. Emma opened the door to lead them out. "I guess," she smiled, "you could call this the blind leading the seeing."

And with that, Emma and her seeing-eye dog, Missy, led her troop of hungry ducks to the cafeteria.

十月之湖

佚名

　　十月，树叶已飘落湖面。在晴朗的日子里无数的树叶散落在颜色渐渐深浓的湖上，大部分是白杨树叶。高大的白杨在无风的日子里依然颤抖，小船般的黄色叶片纷纷从高高的树上坠落，淅淅沥沥，好像雨点落下。下过雨后，树叶被风刮走，湖面上一片冷清，只有睡莲的叶片还残留着。在盛夏时节仿佛翡翠一般的圆叶已经变成浅黄的残片。而那些含苞待放时黄色的睡莲花蕾，像水中游动的小蛇一般，也不复存在。曾经茂密的芦苇变得疏朗，在风霜侵袭下变成很多乱糟糟的箩筐一般的小洲。湖中的水鸟和黑野鸡一听见陌生的声响便躲在了这些小洲底下。

　　整个夏天，水鸟们在睡莲中间过着迷惑的日子。它们没有地方可以尽情嬉戏，整天都在这片睡莲覆盖的水面之间缓缓前行，一会歪歪头，一会儿垂下脑袋。充满睡莲的世界让它们不知所措，好像置身冰雪覆盖的世界。秋季时，在干净的水面上它们会比较活跃。湖面很长，但是除了两处小岛之外都连成一片。湖上的鸟儿会突如其来地上下翻飞，不停地起飞降落，仿佛成群的黑色水上飞机。相较之下，野鸭飞来的速度要快得多，十分壮观。一些雄鸭脖子上的羽毛闪动着深绿色绸缎一般的光芒，他们降落的姿势仿佛一个飞行中队在长期飞行之后初次落地。

　　钓鱼则要等到夏季末了。干旱之后水面变浅了，成群的黑色鱼儿游到水面上来晒太阳，它们十分胆小，很容易被惊动，难以捕捉。要等到傍晚的时候，天气变得凉爽，水面变得昏暗，平静的湖面被鱼群的游动打破，这时才有可能钓上一两条。比如一条幼小的鲈鱼,或者一条比沙丁鱼还小的鳊鱼也许会上钩。在这个季节,尤其是晴朗而炎热的早晨,十到二十几条大个梭子鱼会聚在湖心水面,就那样一动不动,像一群黑色的电鳐。偶尔会突然地骚乱,在水面激起层层的涟漪。

水中和水边的生命都和水相关,这看来似乎有点奇怪。除了一两只急躁不安的鹌鹑在湖畔的杞树下以及唱歌的知更鸟之外,所有在十月的午后从岛上到湖面所有的鸟儿都是水鸟。白嘴鸦很少到这里来,燕八哥也是如此。有时一只鸽子从水面掠过,飞入林中。甚至海鸥也变成了田野上的鸟类。野天鹅常常在春天回到黄色的芦苇丛中筑巢,还有两只高大的苍鹭也每天来到水边的沼泽漫步,听到响声就高高地抬起头。鹬鸟也常常在沼泽中活动,那里的莎草长得像棕色的鸟羽。有时,一只翠鸟会以出乎意料的速度闪电般穿过水面最窄处桤树下的阴暗树影。也有很多时候这里是一片长时间的寂静。水面上慢慢静默下来,没有鱼儿跳出水面打破沉寂,水鸟也不再鸣叫,树叶也不再从十月的空中飘落,深红色的浮萍在平滑的水面上凝固不动。

湖在这样晴朗而安静的日子里显得五彩缤纷。南岸长着白杨、桤树、桉树,以及七叶树,倒映在水中的是黄色和青铜色的光影。果园长着樱桃和梨子,繁盛得一片火红。柳树叶子都要掉光了,衬映着低垂的橙红之焰。橡树依旧翠绿,远处的山毛榉像一片红色的山峰。湖面上更加色彩绚烂,岛上长满了温柏树,虽然树叶还是浓绿,但是枝叶间已经是硕果累累,成熟地悬挂着好像盏盏金色的灯,只是没有人采摘。

October Lake

Anonymous

The October leaves have fallen on the lake. On bright, calm days they lie in thousands on the now darkening water, mostly yellow flotillas of poplar,floating continuously down from great trees that themselves shake in the windless air with the sound of falling water, but on rainy days they seem to swim or be driven away, and nothing remains to break the surface except the last of the olive—yellow lily pads that in high summer covered every inch of water like plates of emerald porcelain. The lilies have gone too, the yellow small—headed kind that in bud are like swimming snakes, and the great reeds are going, woven by wind and frost into untidy basket islands under which coot and moorhen skid for cover at the sound of strangers.

All summer, in this world of water—lilies, the coot and moorhen lived a bewildered life. There was no place where they could swim, and all day they could be seen walking daintily, heads slightly aside and slightly down, cross the lily hidden water, as bemused by the world of leaves as they had been in winter by the world of ice. In unbroken expect for two small islands. This birds, as the fit takes them. dash madly up and down it, taking off and touching down like small fussy black sea—planes. Beside them the arrival of the wild duck, at much higher speed, is almost majestic. They plane down, the necks of the drakes shining like royal green satin, with the air of squadrons coming in after long flights from home.

It was not until late summer fishing was possible. The water was so low and clear after drought that the fish could be seen in great dark shoals, sunning themselves, shy, impossible to catch. Only in the evenings, as the air cooled and the water darkened, and the surface was broken with the silver dances of the rising shoals, would you perhaps get a bite or two, a baby perch sucking at the worm, a roach no bigger than a sardine. All the time, on bright hot mornings especially, great pike would lie out in the middle of the lake in shoals of ten or even twenty, like black torpedoes, transfixed, never moving except in sudden immense rises that rocked the water–surface with rings.

It is curious, but all the life on and about water seems to belong to water.Except for a solitary wren fidgetings delicately about the banks under the alder trees, or a robin singing in the October aflemoon across the water from the islands, all the bird–life is that of water birds. Rooks never seem to come here,nor starlings; an occasional pigeon flaps across to the woods; even the sea–gulls belong to the ploughed land. But wild swans come back to nest in the piles of fawn–colored reeds in the spring, and two great herons stalk the water–meadows every day, struggling ponderously upwards at the sound of voices. Snipe whirl away across the tussocks of brown–quilled sedge on the adjacent marshland, and a solitary kingfisher breaks with magic electric streaks the dark enclosures under the alders that span the narrowest water. But something, and for long periods, there is no life and no sound at all. The water is slowly stilled after the last fish have broken it, the coot are silent, the leaves cease their shaking and falling in the dead October air. The crimson float comes to rest on water that seems to have on it a skin of oil.

On such still clear days the color is wonderful. From the south bank of the water poplar and alder and ash and horse–chestnut let fall high liquid curtains of lemon and bronze. Orchards of cherry and pear smoulder with drooping orange flames beyond the light wall of almost naked willows. The oaks are still green, but the beeches in the distances stand like red mountains. And on the lake itself unexpected color springs up: an island of quince trees, still green, but hung with many ripe lanterns of bright fruit that no one gathers.

关于"建议"

佚名

韦氏字典中"建议"一词的定义如下："对某种行为提出意见或忠告。"

"我需要点建议"是英文语言中很令人厌恶的话语之一。之所以这样说,是因为在无任何预兆的情况下,给建议的人总要面对那些未知的事情。在这方面,我的女儿是专家。最近,我总能预测到她打电话的时间,而且总是在万事如意的情况下,电话铃就响起。犹如我总是向女儿暗示:我已经准备好了! 对于这种无法逃避的事,我总是心态坦然。"爸爸",电话总是这样开始,其实"爸爸"这个词,无论怎样叫,都无所谓。听起来就像问别人问题,又不想让人听到似的。也就是说,她的声音比耳语还要低。我知道,她知道我在听电话,因为是她拨的电话,而她也听出了我的声音,对此我深信不疑。而爸爸这个词好像是我必须准备好的信号。

女儿年幼时,我渴望给她建议。事实上,她也会很高兴地接受,这一点我很肯定。让孩子对生活有所准备,是作为父亲最重要的事情。对此,倒不是我已做好准备,但至少我已在社会上生存这么多年。她过去常常坐在我身旁,或趴在我膝上,让我给她解释她生活中的困惑。我会给她讲伦理和道德,让生活更有意义。几年后,女儿到了花季年龄,不再像儿时那样接受我的建议了。事实上,看得出来,她对此已有些畏惧。我希望她能平稳地度过花季,所以无论怎样,我还是给了她建议。我非常理解,为何她不接受我的建议和我积累的经验。多年来,她都未曾向我征求过建议,但我还是给她提出。现在想想,父亲当年也是这样!

时光如梭,她离开了家,开始了自己的生活。似乎相隔两处,某些事情反倒成为必要,她再次向我征求建议。首先这很好,从这件事上可以看出,她觉得我的智慧还是能经受住时间考验的。但到后来,我觉得我有时也犯错。因此,对她的问题,我开始有点怕回答了。

在我的一生中,并不只有女儿向我征求意见。妻子总是做事诡秘,她知道如何解决问题,但总是希望我们俩的答案能一致。有时,她也接受我的建议,但基本上,还是自己做决定。其他时候,她则神经兮兮地看着我,那种表情似乎在问:"你是哪个星球来的?"不管使用哪种方式,我都尽量使她满意。

生命中,很多时候,都是父母教我为人处世的方法,他们依据自己多年的处世经验帮我做出正确的选择。但现在,他们反而向我征求建议,这倒让我难以理解了。我们似乎互换了角色。这种角色的互换意味着,他们意识到我已经能正确地做出选择,是在夸我。现在,假如我自己也能意识到这一点,那么我又有了新的角色。

亲人们总是将他们的问题在即将抉择的那刻提出,然后等待我给出建议。我不喜欢在这样的情况回答问题,假如说他们愈加僵化,那就等于说自己大无可用之处了。我尽可能地做出回答,并祈祷我的建议能对他们有所帮助,然而我又怎能知道所有的事情?这和给女儿建议不同,给父母建议,就需要设身处地思考。她们向我咨询,就是对我的信任,正如我一直相信他们那样。

我是一名高中老师,我的学生将会考入大学,或参军,或工作。每天,都会有学生问我如何规划未来之类的问题,而不是咨询如何学好功课。很多人还未意识到,高中毕业是人生的关键转折点之一。也的确如此,这些年轻的孩子们正在离开一个占据他们生命四分之三的时代。

因此,在他们离开校园的那刻,我告诉他们,什么行业是朝阳行业,以及他们要服什么样的兵役,以便实现自己的梦想。有时,我只告诉这些年轻的孩子——生活是美好的,他们正处于人生最美好的阶段,即将长大成人,应该说是很幸运的。每次他们离开时,我都祈祷自己的建议会对他们有所帮助。我知道我只能做到这一点了。

偶尔,素未相识的人也向我征求建议。学生家长常问我怎样做,孩子才会前途光明。有时也会问,怎样才能让孩子听他们的话或者相信他们。我想,他们之所以问我,是因为他们确信我知道答案,或者他们看看我的头发变白了,胡子也白了,所以相信,我这个岁数足以解决这些问题。

韦氏关于"建议"一词的定义,最关键问题是:没考虑建议者。给出建议的人理解这个问题,能帮忙解决吗?我给过女儿、父母、学生和陌生人正确的答案吗?

我觉得我该打电话给女儿了,向她征求些建议。

Word on Advice

Anonymous

Webster defines advice as being,"a recommendation with regard to a course of action."

The expression,"I need some advice"has to be one of the most horrifying statements in the English language. What makes it remarkably terrifying is that the advisor is usually confronted with it out of the blue and with little or no warning. My daughter is an expert at this. Lately I have been able to predict when she will call. It usually happens when I am having the type of day when everything seems to be going well. I am actually relaxed with few things that have to be done. It is almost as if I send out a signal to her that I am ready for the challenge. The call always begins with the expression, "Dad". The word is not as important as how it is stated. It sounds like a question being asked by someone who does not want to be heard. In other words, it is a little quieter than a whisper. I know she knows it is I, because she did the calling and I am confident that she knows the sound of my voice.It is almost as if the word is a signal that I had better be ready.

When my daughter was small I looked forward to giving her advice. In fact, I sincerely believe that she also enjoyed it. For the most important thing a Dad can do is get his child ready for life. Not that I ever thought I was ready but at least I have been able to survive my years, so far. She used to sit real close to me or on my lap and I would explain the mysteries of life to her. I would tell her of morals and ethics that made life as good as it can possibly be. Years later, when my daughter hit the wonderful teenaged years,she didn't accept my advice as she did in the past. In fact, she obviously dreaded it. However, I gave it to her anyway because I wanted her to survive her teenaged years. I survived them so why shouldn't she listen to me and take in the knowledge that I had from the experiences of my past. For

智慧英文励志篇

years she never came to me for advice but I continued to submit it. Now that I think of it, my father did the same.

Soon, too soon, she left and started her own life. It was as though our separation necessitated that she would once again need, and seek out, my advice. At first this was a good thing, in that I appreciated the fact that she thought my wisdom was worth the time. After a while I came to the realization that I might not always be right. I started to fear my own answers to her questions.

My daughter is not the only person in my life that asks for advice. My wife does it in an odd way. I know she knows the answer to her question but it is almost as though she wants to combine mine with hers. Sometimes when I give her advice she takes it in and basically makes her own decisions.Other times she gives me that odd look that asks, "What planet were you born on?" Either way I do my best.

My parents have started to ask for my advice. This was very difficult for me to understand. Most of my life my father and mother were the ones to direct me on how I should handle certain situations. They were the ones who survived their years so that they could direct me toward correct decisions.Now the roles seem to be reversed. I guess I should take it as a compliment because this shifting of roles means that they have finally come to the realization that I am capable of making correct choices. Now, if I could only believe this same realization and finally relax in my new role.

My folk's questions usually surround their preparation for the final stages of their lives. I hate these situations because, if I admit that they are getting old, I am literally resigning myself to the fact that I am not far off. I answer their questions as best as I can, praying that I am advising them to do the right things but how could I possibly know? Unlike giving advice to my daughter, giving advice to my parents involves me guessing what to do without the experience of going through what they are presently going through. I guess they ask me because they trust me, like I have always trusted them.

I am a teacher. In fact, I am a high school teacher who works with young adults who are about to embark on careers that include college, the military, or work. Every day I am asked questions concerning how they should organize for their futures, away from a life that centered on their public school. Most people don't realize that graduating from high school is one of the last "rights of passage" our society has. This is tree because these young children are leaving a time that had taken up over 75% of their young lives.

So, I advice them as to what industries will be important when they get out of college; what military service they should look into, in order to achieve what they think they want to achieve. Sometimes just to tell these young men and women that life is a wonderful thing and that they are fortunate to be in a stage of their lives where they are about to become adults. Every time they leave I pray that I gave them good advice. I know I did my best.

Sometimes people I don't know ask for my advice. The parents of my students usually ask what they should do to make their child's future bright. Sometimes they ask what they should do because their child doesn't listen or doesn't believe what they are telling them. I assume they ask me because they believe a teacher should know the answers. Either that or they look at my gray hair and beard and believe that my age necessitates my ability to know.

The basic problem with Webster's definition of advice is that it doesn't take into account the advisor. Does the advisor understand the problem and have the ability to help with a decision. In the past. did I give my daughter, parents, students, and strangers the correct advice?

I think I'll give my daughter a call and ask her for some advice!

不要再和我吻别了

佚名

董事会的会议结束了。鲍勃起身时，不小心撞到了桌子，把杯中的咖啡洒在了会议记录本上。"这是多么让人尴尬的事情啊！没想到人老了以后会变得如此笨拙。"听罢，在座的所有人都笑了。不一会儿，大家开始讲起自己最尴尬的事。轮到弗兰克时，他正安静地坐在那里听别人讲呢。这时，有人说道："快点儿啊，弗兰克，给我们讲讲你最尴尬的时刻吧！"

弗兰克笑了笑，开始向我们讲起他的童年："我在圣萨尔瓦多长大。父亲是一个渔夫，他深深地爱着大海。虽说他有自己的渔船，可是想以捕鱼为生仍然十分艰难。父亲总是很卖力地工作，每次他都会在外面捕够足以养活一家人的鱼后才会回来。事实上他要养活的不仅仅是我们自己的小家，还有爷爷奶奶以及家中的其他孩子们。"说到这儿，弗兰克停顿了一下，看了看我们，接着说道："真希望你们能见到我父亲。他是一个高大而又强壮的人，能够拥有这样的体魄是因为他每天都拉网、与大海'斗争'。当你靠近他的时候，就会闻到海的味道。他总是穿着破旧不堪的帆布衣服，总把雨帽拉到眉毛以下。只要是父亲穿过的衣服，无论母亲洗上多少遍，它们还是会有一种混合着大海和鱼腥的味道。"说到这儿，弗兰克的声音变得有些低沉了。

"天气恶劣的时候，他会亲自开车送我去学校。他有一辆用来载鱼的卡车，它比父亲还要年长。一开起来，它就喀哒喀哒地响，几个街区以外都能听到它的声音。每当他开着这辆老卡车送我上学时，我就会蜷缩在座位里，恨不得让自己马上消失。到了学校，他总是来个急刹车，老卡车就会喷出一团浓浓的烟雾。这时，父亲才会停下来，一时间好像所有的人都赶来看热闹了。接着，他会俯下身子在我的面颊上用力地亲吻一下，告诉我一定要做个乖孩子。那时候，我真是尴尬极了。毕竟我已经12岁了。可是爸爸还是用这样的方式与我道别。"

弗兰克停了一下，又继续说道："我仍清楚地记得那天。我终于鼓足勇气要对父亲说，我已经长大了，不要再以亲吻的方式与我道别了。当我们走到学校时，他停下了车，微笑着向我俯下身来，可我却伸出手来阻止了他，并且说道：'不要，爸爸，我已经长大了，不要再和我吻别了。'那是我第一次用这种口气和父亲说话，我看得出，他很吃惊。我说：'爸爸，我真的已经长大了。不要再和我吻别了。'父亲久久凝视着我，眼中慢慢溢出泪水，我从未见过父亲哭。他转身向车窗外望去。'你说得对，'他说道，'你现在是个大男孩儿了……是个男人了。我以后不会再亲你了。'"

此刻，弗兰克浮现出一种奇怪的表情，他说这些话的时候，眼中满是泪水："不久以后，我父亲再次出海，可是，他却再也没有回来。那天，船队里几乎没有船只出海，除了父亲的船。因为他还有一大家子的人要养活。后来，人们在海上发现了父亲的船，一张渔网一半搭在船上，一半飘浮在海面上。他肯定是遇到了大风，他想尽力保住渔网和鱼钩。"

我看了看弗兰克，他已泪流满面。

弗兰克接着说道："朋友们，我愿意付出任何代价，来换回父亲一个吻……让我感受到他久经风霜的脸……闻闻他身上大海的味道……重温他拥抱我的感觉。我真希望那时的自己真的长大了，因为，如果我真的长大了，就绝不会对父亲说：'我已长大了，不要再和我吻别了。'"

A Goodbye Kiss

Anonymous

The Board Meeting had come to an end. Bob started to stand up and jostled the table, spilling his coffee over his notes. "How embarrassing. I am getting so clumsyin my old age." Everydne had a good laugh, and soon we were all telling stories of our most embarrassing moments. It came around to Frank who sat puietly listening to the others. Someone said, "come on,Frank. Tell us your most embarrassing moment."

Frank laughed and began to tell us of his childhood. "I grew up in San Pedro.My Dad was a fisherman, and he loved the sea. He had his own boat, but it was hard making a living on the sea. He worked hard and would stay out until he caught enough to feed the family. Not just enough for our family, but also for his Mom and Dad and the other kids that were still at home." He looked at us and said, "I wish you could have met my Dad. He was a big man, and he was strong from pulling the nets and fighting the seas for his catch. When you got close to him, he smelled like the ocean. He would wear his old canvas, foul–weather coat and his bibbed overalls.His rain hat would be pulled down over his brow. No matter how much my Mother washed them, they would still smell of the sea and of fish." Frank's voice dropped a bit.

"When the weather was bad he would drive me to school. He had this old truck that he used in his fishing business. That truck was older than he was. It would wheeze and rattle down the road. You could hear it coming for blocks. As he would drive toward the school, I would shrink down into the seat hoping to disappear. Half the time, he would slam to a stop and the old truck would belch a cloud of smoke.He would pull right up in front, and it seemed like everybody would be standing around and watching. Then he would lean over and give me a big kiss on the cheek and tell me to be a good boy. It was so embarrassing for me. Here, I was twelve years old, and my Dad would lean over and kiss me goodby! ”

He paused and then went on, “I remember the day I decided I was too old for a goodbye kiss. When we got to the school and came to a stop, he had his usual big smile. He started to lean toward me, but I put my hand up and said,'No, Dad,'it was the first time I had ever talked to him that way, and he had this surprised look on his face. I said, 'Dad, I'm too old for a goodbye kiss. I'm too old for any kind of kiss.'My Dad looked at me for the longest time, and his eyes started to tear up. I had never seen him cry. He turned and looked out the windshield. 'You're right,'he said. 'You are a big boy a man. I won't kiss you anymore.'”

Frank got a funny look on his face, and the tears began to well up in his eyes,as he spoke. “It wasn't long after that when my Dad went to sea and never came back. It was a day when most of the fleets stayed in, but not Dad. He had a big family to feed. They found his boat adrift with its nets half in and half out. He must have gotten into a gale and was trying to save the nets and the floats.”

I looked at Frank and saw that tears were running down his cheeks.

Frank spoke again. “Guys, you don't know what I would give to have my Dad give me just one more kiss on the cheek to feel his rough old face to smell the ocean on him to feel his arm around my neck. I wish I had been a man then. If I had been a man, I would never have told my Dad I was too old for a goodbye kiss.”

等待清风

佚名

在开始省电的第一天晚上,气温不过30度。我们不觉得难受,3个孩子却抱怨连天。他们是在22度的温室里被呵护长大的,与外面的炎热世界隔绝。

"怎么把这些窗户打开呀?"丈夫摇晃着窗户插销,终于打开了一扇。窗沿上布满了各种各样的昆虫尸体。随着窗户被一扇一扇地打开,喧闹的夜声从外面纷涌而至。

"太热了!怎么睡啊!"13岁的女儿不停地嘀咕着。"我快被热死了!"她弟弟的牢骚也从走廊的另一头传了过来。"今晚就试试好吗?"我对他们说。我实在是太累了,根本不想和他们多说什么。脸上汗涔涔的,但我还是静静地躺着,听着窗外蟋蟀的鸣唱,不禁让我回忆起了童年。邻居家的狗突然间狂叫起来,可能是乱窜的松鼠的声音惊动了它。多年以来,我都没有静下心来真正聆听夜的倾诉了。

我想起了活到92岁的外婆,直到去世的前几个星期,她还在帮妈妈照料花园。恍惚间,我好像又回到了外婆的小屋,回到小时候的炎炎夏日。我把枕头挪到外婆的床尾,转过脸来,面对着开着的窗户,还是热。于是我不停地翻动枕头,想捕捉一丝凉意。

外婆看我翻来覆去地睡不着,就说:"等着起风吧,一会儿就凉快了。"她把百叶帘卷了起来,我盯着那薄薄的白窗帘,盼着它飘动起来。

就这样静静地躺着,等待着,突然,窗外的世界引起了我的注意。昆虫在轻唱,夜深了,邻居们还坐在门廊上聊天,听着他们模糊不清的说话声,我开始慢慢进入梦乡。

"等着风起来吧。"外婆轻声说,我诺诺地应着。虫子撞在纱窗上,砰砰作响。三个街区外,传来火车隆隆驶过的声音。一阵新割青草的清香飘过来,沁人心脾。我还听到了一种说不清的声音——或许是树枝扫过邻家店铺的屋顶吧。一阵睡意袭来,眼皮发沉了,我昏昏欲睡,可我还是盯着窗帘。它飘动起来了……

"妈妈,你听到了那个声音了吗?"7岁的儿子突然嚷了起来,往昔的回忆倏然而去,"我想那是猫头鹰一家吧?""可能是,"我告诉他,"接着听吧……" 没有了空调的嗡嗡作响,房间里格外安静,夜籁之声未经过滤,似乎近在咫尺,触手可及。我希望,当今晚第一缕清风悄然而至时,我仍醒着。

Waiting for the Breeze

Anonymous

On this first night of our cost-cutting adventure, it's only 30 degrees. We're not going to suffer, but the three kids grumble anyway. They've grown up in 22-degree comfort, protected from the heat outside.

"How do you open these windows?" my husband asks. Shaking the window handle, he finally releases one. Lots of dead insects lie on the windowsill. As we spring the windows one by one, the night noises howl outside—and in.

"It's too hot to sleep," my 13-year-old daughter moans. "I'm about to die from this heat," her brother yells down the corridor. "Just try it tonight," I tell them. In truth I'm too tired to argue for long. My face is sweaty, but I lie quietly listening to the cricket choirs outside that remind me of childhood. The neighbor's dog howls. No doubt a squirrel. It's been years since I've taken the time to really listen to the night.

I think about Grandma, who lived to 92 and still managed the upkeep of my Mom's garden until just a few weeks before she died. And then, I'm back there at her house in the summer heat of my childhood. I move my pillow to the foot of Grandma's bed and angle my face toward the open window. I flip the pillow, hunting for the cooler side.

Grandma sees me tossing and tuming. "If you'll just watch for the breeze," she says, "you'll cool off and fall asleep." She raises the Venetian blinds. I stare at the filmy white curtain, willing it to flutter.

Lying still, waiting, I suddenly notice the life outside the window. The bug chorus shouts. Neighbors, sitting on their verandas until late, speak in flowing drawl that soothes me.

"Keep watching for the breeze," Grandma says softly, and I "uh—huh" in reply. Bugs ping the screen. Three blocks away a train rumbles by.

I catch the scent of fresh grass clippings. Then I hear something I can't decode— perhaps a tree branch scratching the shop roof next door.

Sleepy—eyed now, I look at the curtain. It moves...

"Mom, did you hear that?" my seven—year old blurts, tearing me from memories of old. "I think it was an owl family."

"Probably," I tell him. "Just keep listening..."

Without the droning air conditioner, the house sounds are different, more peaceful, and with the windows open outside noises seem close enough to touch. I hope I'm awake tonight when the first breeze sneaks in.

感谢你运送我们的礼物

佚名

我丈夫是一位卡车司机。

他在一家公司工作,这家公司非常好,确保他能在家和家人一起过年过节。但是许多卡车司机的假日是在路上度过的。

这些人在卡车休息站与几乎是完全陌生的人过圣诞节。妻子儿女,以及家人无法和他们共度假日。我想若能对那些无法回家的司机道谢,真是太好了。

如果没有这些卡车司机,住在美国的人,就没礼物可买,没食物可买给家人用餐。这清单可是长而又长。

我知道外面流传着许多关于卡车司机的坏话。

作为一名卡车司机的妻子,我和先生一起上过路;这行可不是好干的。是呀,大家说这些人只是闲坐开车,这又有什么难呢?开车不难;难得的是他们难能与亲人在一块儿,错过子女的生日,或与妻子结婚的周年纪念。而且很多地方很危险,下车都要为生命提心吊胆;还有那些专门勾搭卡车师傅的女人。

诸如此类,卡车师傅要注意的事儿太多了。其实最大的问题是妻子家人要为司机师傅提心吊胆。一般人对司机不尊重。除非你开十八轮大卡车,否则你实在无法知道操作起来有多难。事情并不是这样的——一辆小汽车插到你前面,你就可以在极短距离内停下来。大家塞车时,插到他们前面,或诅咒他们,只因车载重荷,一旦停下来,要一会儿才能再开动。最糟糕的是,搞不好随时都有丧命的危险呢。

半夜电话铃响时,你的心一下子跳到嗓子眼——只有妻子和家人才能了解和卡车司机结婚是什么样子。

为了给大家运送圣诞物品准备过节,卡车司机师傅开长途。我们应该对这些司机师傅说声谢谢;因为是这些司机师傅将货物送到了美国这么多城市。

圣诞节也许有些卡车司机因为不能回家过节而感到孤单。

我希望有人能让他们感受到这一日不同于寻常。

Thanks for Hauling Our Gifts

Anonymous

My husband is a truck driver.

He works for a wonderful company who makes sure that he gets home for the holidays. But,there are a lot of truckers who spend their holidays on the road.

They spend Christmas day in a truck stop with almost total strangers. Many wives, children, and families have to spend the holidays without them. I thought that if would be nice to say thank you to those truckers who don't make it home.

If it weren't for these truckers the people in the USA wouldn't have any presents to buy, no food to buy for their family meal and the list goes on and on.

I know that there are many bad stories out there about truckers.

As a trucker's wife, I have ridden with my husband on the road and it is not an easy life. Yes, people say all they do is sit and drive. What can be hard about that? It isn't the driving that is hard, it is being away from your loved ones, missing a child birthday, or maybe your anniversary and etc. But it is so dangerous out there in many areas that one takes their life in hand just to get out of the truck. All the women who are always trying to Dick a trucker up.

This list goes on and on with all the things truckers have to be on the lookout for. But the biggest problem is the worry that all truckers wives and family goes through. The people

215

out there don't give the truckers the respect they need. Unless you drive an 18-wheeler, you have no idea what it takes to operate one. A car pulls out in front of you and you are to stop on a dime. It doesn't work that way. People who cut them off in a traffic jam, or cuss them out because once they are stopped it takes a while to get going again with a heavy load. Or, the worst of all, is that they will be killed.

When the phone rings in the middle of the night your heart jumps in your throat.But it takes a very special wife and family to understand what it is likebeing married to a trucker.

To all the truckers who have driven the miles and delivered all the Christmas items which the public has purchased for Christmas,they should say thank you to the truckers who brought them to the many cities across the U.S.

Some truckers may be alone on Christmas because they can't get home.

I hope that someone makes the day special for them.

小偷

佚名

　　他第一次注意到那个年轻女人，在航空公司售票处排队买票的时候。她的头发乌黑发亮，在脑后紧紧地打成一个结。他想象着那头秀发披散开来瀑布般落在腰间的情形。只见那女人上身穿着皮外套，肩上挎着一个沉甸甸的黑包，脚上穿着一双黑色软皮靴。她就排在他的前面，他竭尽全力试图看到她的容貌。但是，直到她买好票走开，他才有机会一睹她的芳容：雪白的皮肤，乌黑发亮的眼睛，丰满的嘴唇。他心潮澎湃，狂跳不止。那名年轻女子似乎意识到他在注视着她，便突然垂下了眼睛。

　　他想她可能25岁左右吧，但这种想象突然被售票员的话语打断了。他不再看那女人，然后买了一张到东部一个城市的二等往返机票。

　　距离飞机起飞的时间还有1个小时。为了消磨时间，他走进机场的一家鸡尾酒吧，要了一杯兑水的苏格兰威士忌。他一边慢慢地喝着酒，一边望着大厅里川流不息的乘客——他想，这里面一定有好多漂亮女人都没有结婚，她们穿的是时装杂志上介绍的那种衣服——直到后来他又瞥见了那个穿皮外套的黑发姑娘。她站在旅客服务台旁边，和另外一个姑娘眉飞色舞地聊着什么。那是一位金发碧眼女郎，身穿一件镶着灰色毛皮的布外套。不知怎么回事，他想引起黑发姑娘的注意，想要趁这个姑娘要乘的飞往什么地方去的班机还没有离开之前，请她喝上一杯。然而，尽管他觉得她向他这边张望了一小会儿，但他还是认为自己在酒吧的阴暗处，吸引不了她的秋波。过了没多大一会儿，这两个女人就分手了，但都没有朝这个方向走来。他又要了一杯兑水的苏格兰威士忌。当他再次看见她的时候，他正在买一本杂志，以便在飞机上看。突然，他觉得有人撞到了他。他先是吃了一惊，怎么会有人靠得这么近，甚至碰到了他的身体呢？但等看清此人之后，他的脸上浮起了微笑。

　　"这地方人可真多。"他说。

她抬眼看着他——她是因为害羞，才脸红的吗？——她的嘴角掠过一丝奇怪的表情，但转眼就消失了。她从他的身边走开，加入了大厅的人流之中。

他拿着杂志站在柜台边，但当他将手伸进后边的口袋拿钱夹的时候，发现口袋是空的，里边什么也没有了。他在心里想道：我可能是在什么地方把它弄丢的吧？他开始在脑海里清点装在钱夹里的信用卡、钞票、会员证、身份证等东西。一种恐惧感使他的胃部剧烈地痉挛起来。那个姑娘挨我那样近，他想——他立刻明白了，是她偷了他的钱夹。

怎么办呢？飞机票还在，装在上衣内袋里是万无一失的——他将手伸到衣服里面，摸了摸装机票的纸袋，才放下心来。他可以乘这班飞机，到了之后他连坐公共汽车的钱都没有了，只能叫人来接。之后再乘飞机回家。但是，在此期间要对那些信用卡失窃采取措施——要打电话，让妻子将放在写字台最上面抽屉里的信用卡号码取出来，和一家信用卡公司通电话——真是麻烦死了，要全部办完，准会要命。怎么办呢？

首先找警察把事情经过，以及那年轻女人的模样告诉他。这女人真可恶，他想，好像对他有意思，站得离他很近，听他说话时她的脸红得是那样妩媚动人——这一切只是要挖空心思想偷他的东西。最让人恼怒的是，原来她脸红不是因为害羞，而是做贼心虚。这该死的骗人的娘们。这些细节还是不给警察说好，单讲她所做的事情、他的钱夹里有什么东西就行了。他咬牙切齿。很可能他再也见不到自己的钱夹了。

他正在考虑为了节省时间，就跟那个站在X射线金属探测器旁边的保安员谈一下。突然，他眼睛一亮，喜出望外——吃惊地看到了那个黑发女人——她就坐在大厅的前窗的那个座位上。在她身后渐浓的暮色中，出租车和私车在慢慢腾腾地移动。她好像在全神贯注地看书。她旁边的座位空着。于是，他坐了下来。

"我正在找你呢。"他说。

她瞟了他一眼，似乎没有认出他是谁。"我不认识你。"她说。

"你不会不认识我的。"

她叹了口气，将书放在一边。"你们这些人怎么光想这个，好像我们女孩子是迷路的小动物。你把我当成什么人了？"

"你摸走了我的钱夹。"他说。他很得意地说"摸走"，他觉得这个字眼比"偷走"、"盗走"，甚至"掏走"，听上去更加贴切。

"你在说什么呀？"那女孩说。

"我知道是你干的——在杂志柜台边。只要你还给我，事情就一笔勾销，否则就把你交给警察。"

她仔细打量着他,神情非常严肃。"好吧,"她说着,将她那只黑包拉到膝盖上,手伸进去,掏出了一只皮夹。

他从她手里一把拿过来。"等一下,"他说,"这不是我的。"

那女孩撒腿就跑,他在后面穷追不舍,周围的人纷纷避开,真像电影中的场面。那女孩飞快地左拐右转,避免发生碰撞。他的喘息声使他想起了自己的年纪,后来他听到一个女人的喊声从后面传来:

"抓、抓贼! 抓住那个男人!"

前面的黑发女人已经转过拐角,不见了踪影。这时,一个身穿海军制服的年轻人伸脚一绊,他猛地跌倒,膝盖和胳膊肘都重重地砸在大厅的地板砖上,但他的手里仍紧紧地攥着那个不属于他的皮夹。

这只皮夹是一名妇女的,鼓鼓囊囊地装着钞票和像"萨克""佩克与佩克""洛德与泰勒"这种公司的信用卡。皮夹的主人是那个穿皮毛镶边外套的金发女人——他早先看到在和那个作贼的黑发女人交谈的金发女人。她也跑得气喘吁吁,像那个和她一同赶来的警察一样。

"就是他,"金发女人说,"是他偷了我的皮夹。"

他突然想到,他甚至无法向警察证实自己的身份。

事隔两星期之后——他不再那样尴尬和恼怒,家庭律师的报酬已经支付,家里的风波也已经过去——他的钱夹在上午送来的邮件中意外地出现了,没有附任何解释。皮夹原封未动,钱一点也没有少,所有的证卡都在。尽管松了口气,但他觉得,在自己今后的人生旅途中,他在警察旁边会感到内疚,在女人们面前会感到羞愧难当。

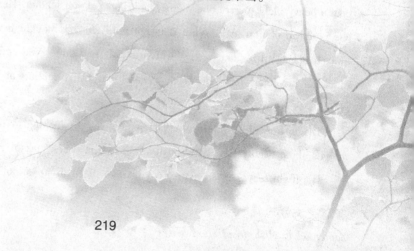

Thief

Anonymous

He is waiting for the airline ticket counter when he first notices the young woman. She has glossy black hair pulled tightly into a knot at the back of her bead–the man imapines it loosed and cascading to the small of her back–and carries over she shoulder of her leather coat a heavy black purse. She wears black boots of soft leather. He struggles to see her face– she is ahead of him in line–but it is not until she has bought her ticket and turns to walk away that he realizes her beauty, which is pale and daN–eyed and full–mouthed, and which quickens his heart beat.She seems aware that he is stating at her and lowers her gaze abruptly.

The airline clerk interrupts. The man gives up looking at the woman—he thinks she may be about twenty–five—and buys a round–trip, coach class ticket to an eastern city.

His flight leaves in an hour. To kill time, the man steps into one of the airport cocktail bars and orders a scotch and water.While he sips it he watches the flow of travelers through the terminal —including a remarkable number, he thinks, of an unattached pretty women dressed in fashion magazine clothes—until he catches sight of the black—haired girl in the leather coat. She is standing near a Travelers Aid counter, deep in conversation with a second girl, a blond in a cloth coat trimmed with gray fur. He wants somehow to attract the brunette's attention, to invite her to have a drink with him before her own flight leaves for wherever she is traveling, but even though he believes for a moment she is looking his way he cannot catch her eye from out of the shadows of the bar. In another instant the two women separate; neither of their direction is toward him. He orders a second Scotch and water.

When next he sees her, he is buying a magazine to read during the flight and becomes aware that someone is jostling him.At first he is startled that anyone would be so close as to touch him, but when he sees who it is he musters a smile.

"Busy place."he says.

She looks up at him—is she blushing? —and an odd grimace crosses her mouth and vanishes. She moves away from him and joins the crowds in the terminal.

The man is at the counter with his magazine, but when he reaches into his back pocket for his wallet the pocket is empty.Where could I have lost it? he thinks. His mind begins enumerating the credit cards, the currency, the membership and identification cards, his stomach churns with something very like fear. The girl who was so near to me, he thinks— and all at oncehe understands that she has picked his poocked.

What is he to do? He still has his ticket, safely tucked inside his suit coat—he reaches into the jacket to feel the envelope, to make sure. He can take the flight, call someone to pick him up at his destination–since he cannot even afford bus fare conduct his business and fly home. But in the meantime he will have to do something about the lost credit cards–call home, have his wife get the numbers out of the top desk drawer, phone the card companies— so difficult a process, the whole thing suffocating.What shall he do?

First,find a policeman, tell what has happened, describe the young woman, damn her, he thinks, for seeming to be attentive to him, to let herself stand so close to him, to blush prettily when he spoke—and all the time she wanted only to steal from him.And her blush was

not shyness but the anxiety of being caught; that was most disturbing of all. damn deceitful creatures. He will spare the policeman the details—just tell what she has down, what is in the wallet. He grits his teeth. He will probably never see his wallet again.

He is trying to decide if he should save time for talking to a guard near the X ray machines when he is appalled—and elated to see the black-haired girl. She is seated against a front window of the terminal, taxis and private cars moving sluggishly beyond her in the gathering darkness: she seems engrossed in a book. A seat beside her is empty, and the man occupies it.

"I've been looking for you." he says.

She glances at him with no sort of recognition. "I don't know you," she says.

"Sure you do."

She sighs and puts the book aside. "Is this all you characters think about picking up girls like we were stray animals? What do you think I am?"

"You lifted my wallet。" he says. He is pleased to have said "lifted", thinking it sounds more wordly than stole Or took or even ripped off.

"I beg your pardon?" the girl says. "I know you did—at the magazine counter. If you'll just give it back, we can forget the whole thing. If you don't, then I'll hand you over to the police."

She studies him, her face serious. "All right," she says. She pulls the black bag onto her lap, reaches into it and draws out a wallet.

He takes it from her. "Wait a minute," he says, "This isn't mine."

The girl runs, he bolts after her. It is like a scene in a movie—bystanders scattering, the girl zigzagging to avoid collisions, the sound of his own breathing reminding him how old he is—until he hears a woman's voice behind him:

"Stop, thief! Stop that man! "

Ahead of him the brunette disappears around a corner and in the same moment a young man in a marine uniform puts out a foot to trip him up. He falls hard, banging knee and elbow on the tile floor of the terminal, but manages to hang on to the wallet which is not his.

The wallet is a woman's, fat with money and credit cards from places like Sak's and Peck & Peck and Lord & Taylor, and it belongs to the blonde in the fur–trimmed coat—the blonde he has earlier seen in conversation with the criminal brunette. She,too, is breathless, as is the police man with her.

"That's him,"the blonde girl says,"He lifted my billfold."

It occurs to the man that he cannot even prove his own identity to the policeman.

Two weeks later—the embarrassment and rage have diminished,the family lawyer has been paid, the confusion in his household has receded the wallet turns up without explanation in one morning's mail. It is intact, no money is missing, all the cards are in place. Though he is relieved, the man thinks that for the rest of his life he will feel guilty around policemen, and ashamedin the presence of women.

雾

乔治·斯莱思·斯特里特

　　无论它是美还是不美，一场伦敦大雾总是有值得大书特书的地方。它能带给我们每时每刻都需要的那种"变化"。最初，这个世界几乎是白茫茫的一片，然后，一点一点地慢慢清晰起来，这和我们平常所见的完全不同。这时，就算是最迟钝的人也不会察觉不到眼前的景物起了变化。这种变化之大，绝不亚于从伦敦来到格拉斯哥。又比如，回到家里，或来到俱乐部，这种平凡单调的日常琐事，在雾天也几乎成为惊人的壮举，完成之后不免要深深地松一口气，自幸安全脱险——这时人们至少会得到一种不同寻常的新鲜之感。这时我们已经不像是一个到俱乐部去玩的人，而像是一个航行遇险的海员在九死一生之际，终于得救，并且受到一群以前非常淡漠而这时却非常激动的侍者们的热烈欢迎。的确，一场迷雾带给伦敦人的变化非常之大，比起去里维埃拉避雾度假所带来的变化都要大。其次，雾还能使人的善良之心和喜悦之情充分表现出来，这是伦敦人引以为荣的两大特点。当然，它也会把富人的那种极度自私自利揭露出来。那些几乎是无忧无虑地活在世上的人，自然会因为这点儿小小不便或哀声叹气，或咒骂不已。但是为生计奔波的伦敦人，比如那些马车夫和汽车司机，比如你和我，却会把我们那种欢快心情充分展现出来。某个星期一，我在海德公园拐角那个街区的一辆公共汽车上乘坐了半个小时，一路上与司机攀谈。人们往往会对汽车司机感到失望，因为他们认为他应该喋喋不休，咒骂不已，而他却没有这类长处。但是我们应该看到，这是个工作非常辛苦但却又非常快乐的人,非常勤快,服务周到,笑口常开。他在自己的工作方面是个行家——这点在雾天最能突出显示出来——而他工作起来十分熟练,对于那种凭借经验,总以为从事具体行业的人往往不是愚蠢就是冒失,因而对绝大多数都不称职的人士来说,总是一件快事吧。最后我离开他时,他的副手引我绕过车轮马蹄,一直把我送到人行道上,这时我有一种感觉,觉得我的周围的确都是好人。上周日的晚上,我曾步行一英里回到我的寓所,一路上,我每碰到一个人就向他问路。但是没有一个人给予粗鲁甚至简慢的回答,每个人都是彬彬有礼,俏皮风趣,谈古论今,有说有笑。我们这个民族确实是个友好的民族,能体会这一点,即使是遇上一次雾天,也是值得的。雾的另外一种乐趣,就如同我们听到某个百万富翁摔断了腿时所感到的那种乐趣相差无几,只是在性质上比较温和有所淡化而已。那种命运特别好的人往往并不快乐,即使健康状况良好也不能把它驱除掉。在某个街区的一辆宽敞的布鲁厄姆马车上坐着一位派头十足的老头,他口吐白沫,大发雷霆。看到这个情景,人们不禁会想,在这件事上,命运总算暂时是公平的。

　　这些就是我们在一场伦敦的雾中所找到的一些乐趣。

225

Fog

George Slythe Street

Beauty or none, there is much to be said for a London fog. It gives us all that "change" which we are always needing. When our world is all but invisible, and growing visible bit by bit looks utterly different from its accustomed self, the stupidest of us all can hardly fail to observe a change for our eyes at least as great as there would have been in going to Glasgow. When, arriving at one's house or one's club; that monotonous diurnal incident seems an almost incredible feat, accomplished with profound relief and gratitude for a safe deliverance, one has at least an unaccustomed sensation. One is not a man going into his club, but a mariner saved from shipwreck at the last gasp, to be greeted with emotion by erst indifferent waiters. Yes, a fog gives Londoners a more thorough change than going to the Riviera to avoid it. Then it brings out the kindness and cheerfulness, which are their prime claim to honour, into strong relief. True, it also throws into relief the incomparable egoism of the prosperous among them. People with no serious cares or worries in the world of course bemoan and upbraid this trifling inconvenience. But the working, struggling Londoners, cabmen and busmen, you and I, display our indomitable good-humour to advantage. I stayed on top of a bus for half an hour in the block on Monday at Hyde Park Corner and talked with the driver. People are often disappointed in a busdriver because they expect a wit and a

pretty swearer. They find neither, but they find an overworked man of extraordinary cheerfulness, responsive, ready to laugh. He is master of his business — a fact emphasised by the fog — to a degree refreshing to one whose experience of men professing some practical calling is that the great majority, some from mere stupidity, some from over-hasty enthusiasm, are quite incompetent. When finally I left him, his mate piloted me through wheels and horses to the pavement, and I felt I had been among folk who deserve to live.On Sunday night I walked a mile to my abode, and made a point of asking my whereabouts of every one I met. Not one churlish or even hurried answer: politeness, jokes, reminiscences, laughter.We are a kindly people, and it is worth a fog to know it. Another pleasure of a fog is a mild but extended form of the pleasure we feel when we hear that a millionaire has broken his leg. The too fortunate are suffering a discontent health cannot remove. There was in that block a fat brougham containing an important-looking old man who foamed at the mouth, and one reflected that there was a temporary equality of fortunes.

Such are the pleasures we may take in a London fog.

蚯蚓

佚名

世界各地都有蚯蚓，它们有助于建造世界，它们有助于土地里长出人类所需的粮食。你觉得这种说法很奇怪吗？

现在，让我们来看看蚯蚓是怎么做到这些的吧。蚯蚓在地下生存，它们在地下钻来钻去，把泥土钻成一条条蜿蜒绵长的孔道，如同街道一般。那些"长廊"或者"隧道"可以使泥土疏松，从而有利于植物的根部生长。

这些孔道也有助于空气轻易地进入泥土。蚯蚓在泥土里不停地钻来钻去，就如同人们在地面上用耙子、铲或犁松土一样。

蚯蚓首要的工作还是使土壤更加肥沃。当它们建造房子的时候，总是让自己长长的身体里装满泥土，并把它带到地上，堆成小堆，这就是人们所称的蚯蚓粪。每天早上或下雨之后，你都可以在花园的小径上发现蚯蚓粪。

每年都有成千上万的蚯蚓在忙碌着，它们每年可以挖动数以吨计的泥土。它们用嘴使泥土疏松并使之变得肥沃。那些本来是硬如坚石的土壤，经它们钻动之后就变得肥沃而精细了。

The Earthworm

Anonymous

Earthworms are found in all parts of the world. They help to build the world. They help to prepare the earth to bring forth the food of man. Do you think that very strange?

Now let us see how this is done. The worms live underground.They make long, winding halls, like streets, some inches below the top soil. The halls or little tunnels help to keep the earth loose,so that the fine roots of the plants can grow well in it.

These tunnels also serve to help the air move more easily through the soil. By their constant motion below the surface the worms till the earth, as rakes, spades, or ploughs till it above.

The chief work of the earthworms is to enrich the soil. When they make their houses, they fill their long bodies with the earth,and carry it to the top of the ground. There they pile it in heaps,called worm-casts. Early in the day or after a rain you can find these worm-casts over all the garden paths.

There are so many worms busy all the time that each year they bring up tons of earth. They make the earth fine and loose by pinching it off with their mouths. Fields once stony and hard have become rich and fine.

助人

一个人处于逆境时,一点点的帮助远远胜过千万句的祈祷。

这是寒冬中的一个星期天。教堂的停车场很快就停满了车子。我下车的时候,注意到教友们一边往教堂走,一边窃窃私语。

我走近一点儿,看见一个男人斜倚在教堂外面的墙上。他几乎是躺在那里,仿佛睡着了似的。他穿着一件破破烂烂的防水外衣,带着一顶帽子,帽子拉下来遮住了他的脸。他脚上那双鞋似乎已经穿了30年,鞋子很小,到处都是洞,脚趾头露在外面。我猜想这是个流浪汉,他可能睡着了,于是我绕过他走进教堂。

人们高兴地聊了一会儿,这时有人提起了躺在外面的那个人。大家窃笑、私语,却没有人,当然也包括我在内,愿意去请他进来。过了一会儿,人们开始做礼拜了。我们都等着传道士到讲坛前给我们布道。就在这时,教堂的门开了,那个流浪汉低着头沿着过道走了进来。

人们倒吸了一口气,小声嘀咕着,扮着鬼脸。那个人径直走到了讲坛,他摘掉了帽子,脱掉了外套,我的心沉了下来。站在那儿的传道士正是那个"流浪汉"。

人们一言不发,屋子里寂静无声。

传道士拿出圣经,放在架子上。

"朋友们,我想我无需再告诉你们我今天要讲的内容是什么了。"

接着他唱起了一首歌:

"如果我在经过的时候帮助了他,

如果我为他唱一首欢快的歌,

或者说一句鼓励的话,

如果我能引导身在歧途的人,

那么我将不会虚度年华。"

Help Somebody

Anonymous

When a person is down in the world, an ounce of help is better than a pound of preaching.

It was a cold winter's day that Sunday. The parking lot to the church was filling up quickly. I noticed as I got out of my car that fellow church members were whispering among themselves as they walked to the church.

As I got closer I saw a man leaned up against the wall outside the church. He was almost lying down as if he was asleep. He had on a long trench coat that was almost in shreds and a hat topped his head, pulled down so you couldn't see his face. He wore shoes that looked 30 years old, too small for his feet, with holes all over them, his toes stuck out. I assumed this man was homeless, and asleep, so I walked on by through the doors of the Church.

We all enjoy fellowship for a few minutes, and then someone brought up the man who was lying outside. People snickered and gossiped, but no one bothered to ask him to come in, including me. A few moments later church began. We all waited for the preacher to take

231

his place, and to give us the word, when the doors to the church opened. In came the homeless man, walking down the aisle with his head down.

People gasped and whispered and made faces. He made his way down the aisle and up onto the pulpit. When he took off his hat and coat, my heart sank. There stood our preacher. He was the "homeless man".

No one said a word. The room was silent and still.

Then the preacher took his Bible and laid it on the stand.

"Folks, I don't think I have to tell you what I'm preaching about today."Then he started singing the words to this sons.

"If I can help somebody as I pass along, if I can cheer somebody with a word or sons, if I can show somebody that he's traveling wrong, then my living shall not be in vain."

饼干

佚名

心里充满阳光才能与人分享。

一个小男孩儿在夏令营期间收到妈妈寄来的一大包饼干。他吃了几块,然后把剩下的放在了床底下。第二天午饭后,小男孩儿去帐篷里拿饼干,饼干却不见了。

有人把这件事告诉了夏令营的指导员。下午的时候,指导员看见另一个小男孩儿坐在大树后面吃着偷来的饼干。他心里暗想:"一定要教育那个年轻人不要偷东西。"

他回到孩子们中间,找到丢饼干的小男孩儿说:"比利,我知道谁偷了你的饼干。你愿意帮我给他一个教训吗?"

"当然——可是您不打算惩罚他吗?"小男孩儿不解地问。

指导员解释说:"不,那样只能让他怨恨你。你打电话给妈妈,让她再给你寄一盒饼干。"

小男孩儿照指导员的话去做了。几天后,他又收到了一盒饼干。

"现在,偷你饼干的人就在湖边。去把你的饼干分给他。"指导员说。

"但是他是个小偷。"小男孩儿抗议。

"我知道,但是你去试一试,看看会发生什么。"

半个小时后,指导员看见两个人手挽手爬上山。偷饼干的小男孩儿坚持把水果刀送给比利,作为偷吃饼干的补偿。可比利却竭力地拒收新朋友的礼物,说吃几块饼干真的没什么大不了的。

Cookies

Anonymous

You have to enjoy the sunshine in your heart before you can spread it to others.

A small boy at summer camp received a large package of cookies in the mail from his mother. He ate a few, then placed the remainder under his bed. The next day, after lunch, he went to his tent to get a cookie. The box was gone.

That afternoon a camp counselor, who had been told of the theft, saw another boy sitting behind a tree eating the stolen cookies. "That young man," he said to himself, "must be taught not to steal."

He returned to the group and sought out the boy whose cookies had been stolen. "Billy," he said, "I know who stole your cookies. Will you help me teach him a lesson?"

"Well, yes, but aren't you going to punish him?" asked the puzzled boy.

"No, that would only make him resent and hate you," the counselor explained. "I want you to call your mother and ask her to send you another box of cookies."

The boy did as the counselor asked and a few days later he received another box of cookies in the mail.

"Now," said the counselor, "the boy who stole your cookies is down by the lake. Go down there and share your cookies with him."

"But, he's the thief." protesteds the boy.

"I know. But try it, and see what happens."

Half an hour later the camp counselor saw the two come up the hill, arm in arm. The boy who had stolen the cookies was earnestly trying to get the other to accept his jackknife in payment for the stolen cookies, and the victim was just as earnestly refusing the gift from his new friend, saying that a few old cookies weren't that important anyway.

最美丽的心

佚名

如果你不想失去美,请把它从你的脸上移入到你的内心吧!

一天,一个年轻人站在镇子中央宣称自己拥有全镇最美丽的心。一大群人围着他,都羡慕他拥有这么完美的、没有一点儿瑕疵的心。大家都认同这确实是他们所见到的最美丽的心。这个年轻人非常骄傲,更加大声地夸耀他的心。

突然,一位老人走到人群前说:"可你的心没有我的心美。"围观的人和年轻人都看着这位老人的心。它强劲有力地跳动着,但却布满伤疤。心上有的地方被撕下了一小块儿,又填补了另外的碎片,但这些碎片不是很适合,所以边缘凹凸不平。实际上,有些地方还有一些很深的坑洞,缺了好多块。

人们看着这颗心,心里想:他怎么能说他的心更美呢?年轻人看着老人的这颗心,大笑道:"您在开玩笑吧。比比看,我的心是完美无瑕的,而您的心却伤痕累累。"

老人说:"是的,你的心看起来是没有瑕疵,但我永远不会拿我的心换你的心。你看,我心上的每道疤痕都表示我曾经把爱奉献给了一个人——我把我的心撕下一块儿给他们,通常他们也会撕下一块儿来填补我的心,因为这些碎片不是正合适,所以边缘会粗糙些,但我很珍惜这些碎片,因为它们使我想起我们分享过的爱。有时候,我把我的心撕下一块儿给别人,却没有换回他们的心。于是就有了这些空洞——奉献也不一定有回报。尽管这些空洞让人心痛,但它们能使我想起我对他们的爱。我希望有一天那些人会用他们的心把这些洞堵上。现在你知道什么是真正的美了吧?"

年轻人默默地站着,泪流满面。他走向老人,伸手从他那颗完美、年轻而又美丽的心上撕下一块儿,然后用颤抖的手把它交给了老人。

老人把这块心放到自己的心上,然后从自己布满伤疤的心上撕下一块放到年轻人的伤口上。这块心很合适,但并不完美,边缘不是很整齐。年轻人看看自己的心,虽然它不再完整,但比以前更美了,因为爱正从老人的心流向他的心。他们彼此拥抱,然后肩并肩地走了。

The Most Beautiful Heart

Anonymous

If you do not want to lose your beauty, move it from your face into your heart.

One day a young man was standing in the middle of the town proclaiming that he had the most beautiful heart in the whole town.A large crowd gathered and they all admired his heart for it was perfect. There was not a mark or flaw in it. Yes, they all agreed it truly was the most beautiful heart they had ever seen. The young man was very proud and boasted more loudly about his beautiful heart.

Suddenly, an old man appeared at the front of the crowd and said,"But your heart is not nearly as beautiful as mine."The crowd and the young man looked at the old man's heart. It was beating strongly, but full of scars. It had places where pieces had been removed and other pieces put in, but they didn't quite fit right and there were several jagged edges. In fact, in some places there were deep gouges where whole pieces were missing.

The people stared — how can he say his heart is more beautiful,they thought. The young man looked at the old man's heart and saw its state and laughed."You must be joking, he said."Compare your heart with mine, mine is perfect and yours is a mess of scars and tears.

"Yes,"said the old man,"yours is perfect-looking but I would never trade with you. You see, every scar represents a person to whom I have given my love — tear out a piece of my heart and give it to them, and often they give me a piece of their heart which fits into the empty place in my heart, but because the pieces aren't exact, I have some rough edges, which I cherish, because they remind me of the love we shared. Sometimes I have given pieces of my heart away,and the other person hasn't returned a piece of his heart to me.These are the empty gouges—giving love is taking a chance.although these gouges are painful, they stay open, reminding me of the love I have for these people too, and I hope someday they may return and fill the space in my heart. So now do you see what true beauty is?"

The young man stood silently with tears running down his cheeks. He walked up to the old man, reached into his perfect young and beautiful heart, and rippeds a piece out. He offered it to the old man with trembling hands.

The old man took his offering, placed it in his heart and then took a piece from his old scarred heart and placed it in the wound in the young man's heart. It fit, but not perfectly, as there were some jagged edges. The young man looked at his heart, not perfect anymore but more beautiful than ever, since love from the old man's heart flowed into his. They embraced and walked away side by side.

给儿子的信

F.D.斯坦厄普

亲爱的孩子：

　　讨人喜欢要有必备的条件，但又是一门不易学到的艺术，很难将其归纳成规则。你自己良好的判断力与观察力将使你领悟比我教授给你的还要多的东西。"己所不欲，勿施于人"，据我所知，这是取信于人的最可靠的办法。细心留意别人怎样做让你愉快，那么很可能你做同样的事也会使别人愉悦。如果别人对你的性情、兴趣甚至弱点甚为关心，让你满心欢喜，那么请相信，你对别人施以同样的热情和关照，也一定会使他们高兴。与人为伴来往时，须适应其中的氛围，勿矫揉造作，发现同伴的幽默之处时，就要诚然开怀一乐，甚至调笑一番，这是每个人对群体应具备的态度。在人前不要说瞎话，没有比这更让人讨厌和不悦的事了。如果你恰好有一则很简短而又相当切题的故事，可用最简洁明了的语言叙述一番。即便如此，也要表示出你并不擅长讲述，而仅是因为它实在太简短才使你情不自禁地这样做。

　　在交谈中，首先要摒弃以自我为中心的癖好，绝不试图让别人对自己的私事或者自己关注的事产生兴趣。尽管这些事情对你来说兴趣盎然，但对于别人却味同嚼蜡，不得要领。再者，个人的私事也不可能永远隐秘。无论你自以为有什么好处，切忌在人前自爱自怜地展示，也不要像许多人那样，挖空心思地引导谈话，以伺机自我表现一番。如果你确有长处，一定会被人发现，不必自己点出，何况这样做最好。当与人有是非之争时，绝不要激动地大喊大叫，即使你自以为正确或者知道自己是正确的，也要善加控制，冷静地说出自己的意见，这是说服人的唯一方法。但如果这样仍不奏效，就试着变个话题，高高兴兴地说："我俩谁也说服不了谁，而且也不是非得说服对方不可，我们讨论别的吧。"

　　要记住，与人交往时要懂得尊重他人习俗的礼仪。在这一群人中恰如其分的话语，对另一群人而言却不适宜。与某些人适宜的幽默、妙语，甚至小小的出格行为，换个地方会显得平淡无奇，或令人苦恼。说一个词儿或者打一个手势，在某群人中即暗示着某种性格、习惯和隐语，而一旦离开那种特定的氛围，就会毫无意义，人们常常在这一点上犯错误。他们喜欢把在某群人、某种环境中的得意言行随意搬到别的地方使用，而此时却风趣尽失，或不合时宜，或张冠李戴而唐突无聊。是的，他们常用这样笨拙的开场白：“告诉你一件很棒的事!”或者“我要告诉你世上最绝妙的……”希望这些话能勾起对方的期待，但结果却是彻底的绝望，使得说这些话的人看起来像个十足的傻子。

如果你获得别人的好感和情感，无论是男人还是女人，都要特别留意去发现他们可能具备的长处，以及他们明显的不足之处。人人都会有缺陷，但要公正而善意地对待别人的这个或那个不足。人人还会有许多过人之处，或者至少具有可以称做优异的地方，尽管人们喜欢听到对其自知的优点的赞美，但他们最感兴趣的仍是对自己渴望具备且尚不自信的长处的赞许。

239

Letter to His Son

D.Stanhope

Dear boy,

The art of pleasing is a very necessary one to possess, but a very difficult one to acquire. It can hardly be reduced to rules; and your own good sense and observation will teach you more of it than I can. "Do as you would be done by." is the surest method that I know of pleasing. Observe carefully what pleases you in others, and probably the same things in you will please others. If you are pleased with the complaisance and attention of others to your humors, your tastes, or your weaknesses, depend upon it, the same complaisance and attention on your part to theirs will equally please them.

Take the tone of the company that you are in, and do not pretend to give it; be serious, gay, or even trifling, as you find the present humor of the company; this is an attention due from every individual to the majority. Do not tell stories in company; there is nothing more tedious and disagreeable; if by chance you know a very short story, and exceedingly applicable to the present subject of conversation, tell it in as few words as possible; and even then, throw out that you do not love to tell stories, but that the shortness of it tempted you.

Of all things banish the egotism out of your conversation, and never think of entertaining people with your own personal concerns or private affairs; though they are interesting to you, they are tedious and impertinent to everybody else; besides that, one cannot keep one's own private affairs too secret. Whatever you think your own excellencies may be, do not affectedly display them in company; nor labor, as many people do, to give that turn to the conversation, which may supply you with an opportunity of exhibiting them.If they are real, they will infallibly be discovered, without your pointing them out yourself,and

智慧英文励志篇

with much more advantage. Never maintain an argument with heat and clamor, though you think or know yourself to be in the right; but give your opinion modestly and coolly,which is the only way to convince; and, if that does not do, try to change the conversation,by saying, with good humor, "We shall hardly convince one another; nor is it necessary that we should, so let us talk of something else."

Remember that there is a local propriety to be observed in all companies; and that what is extremely proper in one company may be, and often is, highly improper in another.The jokes, the bonmots, the little adventures, which may do very well in one company, will seem flat and tedious, when related in another. The particular characters, the habit, the cant of one company may give merit to aword, or a gesture, which would have none at all if divested of those accidental circumstances. Here people very commonly err; and fond of something that has entertained them in one company, and in certain circumstances, repeat it with emphasis in another, where it is either insipid, or, it may be, offensive, by being ill timed or misplaced. Nay, they often do it with this silly preamble: "I will tell you an excellent thing," or "I will tell you the best thing in the world." This raises expectations,which, when absolutely disappointed, make the relaror of this excellent thing look,very deservedly, like a fool.

If you would particularly gain the affection and friendship of particular people,whether men or women, endeavor to find out their predominant excellency, if they have one, and their prevailing weakness, which everybody has; and do justice to the one, and something more than justice to the other. Men have various objects in which they may excel, or at least would be thought to excel; and, though they love to hear justice done to them, where they know that they excel, yet they are most and best flattered upon those points where they wish to excel, and yet are doubtful whether they do or not.

拿破仑致约瑟芬

佚名

我不爱你，一点也不爱你，相反，我讨厌你——你是个顽皮的、笨拙的、愚蠢的灰姑娘。你从不写信给我，你不爱你的丈夫；你明明知道你的信能带给他何等的快乐，但你却不肯草草地写上六行字给他，哪怕是很随便地写上六行。

你整天都在做些什么呢，女士？有什么事情如此重要，以至于让你腾不出一点儿时间写信给你忠诚的爱人？你曾答应过给我温柔而忠诚的爱情，它被什么样的感情窒息和排挤在一边了呢？你那位奇妙的人物，那位新的情人，究竟是何等人物，竟然占去了你每一分钟，占据了你所有的时间，以至于你没有时间对你的丈夫略表关心呢？约瑟芬，当心一些，说不定我会在某个美丽的夜晚破门而入。

事实上，我因为没有你的音信而坐立不安，我的爱人。请马上给我写四页信寄来，四页充满柔情蜜意的信，那样我的心中将充满快乐。

我多希望过不了多久就能把你紧紧地搂在怀里，并用如同赤道下炽热阳光般的热情千万次地亲吻你。

Napoleon Bonaparte to Josephine

Anonymous

I don't love you, not at all, on the contrary, I detest you—You're a naughty, gawky, foolish Cinderella. You never write me, you don't love your husband; you know what pleasure your letters give him, and yet you haven't written him six hnes, dashed off casually!

What do you do all day, Madam? What is the affair so important as to leave you no time to write to your devoted lover? What affection stifles and puts to one side the love, the tender and constant love you promised him? Of what sort can be that marvelous being, that new lover who absorbs every moment, tyrannizes over your days, and prevents your giving any attention to your husband? Josephine, take care! Some fine night, the doors will be broken open, and there I'll be.

Indeed, I am very uneasy, my love, at receiving no news of you; write me quickly four pages, pages full of agreeable things which shall fill my heart with the pleasantest feelings.

I hope before long to crush you in my arms and cover you with a million kisses burning as though beneath the equator.

美丽的祈祷

佚名

我要求上帝去掉我的习惯。

上帝说，不，不是我来拿走，而是你去放弃。

我请求上帝让我残疾的孩子痊愈。上帝说，不，他的灵魂是健康的，他的身体不过是暂时的。

我请求上帝给予我耐性。上帝说，不，耐性是磨难的副产品，它不是给予的，而是学来的。

我请求上帝给我幸福。上帝说，不，我给你祝福，但是幸福要自己去创造。

我请求上帝免除我的痛苦。上帝说，不，痛苦能够让你远离尘世烦扰，使你离我更近。

我请求上帝让我的灵魂成长。上帝说，不，你必须自己成长！但是我会照料你，让你收获丰足。

我请求上帝给予我一切以便我能够享受生活。上帝说，不，我会给你生命，你就可以享受一切了。

我请求上帝帮我爱别人，就像他爱我一样。上帝说，啊，最后你终于明白了。

这一天是你的，不要丢弃。

A Beautiful Prayer

Anonymous

I asked God to take away my habit.

God said, No. It is not for me to take away, but for you to give up.

I asked God to make my handicapped child whole. God said, No. His spirit is whole, his body is only temporary.

I asked God to grant me patience. God said, No. Patience is a byproduct of tribulations; it isn't granted, it is learned.

I asked God to give me happiness. God said, No. I give you blessings;happiness is up to you.

I asked God to spare me pain. God said, No. Suffering draws you apart from worldly cares and brings you closer to me.

I asked God to make my spirit grow. God said, No. You must grow on your own! But I will prune you to make you fruitful.

I asked God for all things that I might enjoy life. God said, No. I will give you life, so that you may enjoy all things.

I ask God to help me LOVE others, as much as He loves me. God said... Ahhhh, Finally you have the idea.

THIS DAY IS YOURS DON'T THROW IT AWAY.